Ways to Play With Words!

A Collection of Word Games & Activities

by
Terri Landers

Missing Piece Press
Kent, Washington

Ways to Play with Words!
A Collection of Word Games and Activities

Copyright © 2004 Terri Landers

Printed in the United States of America

ISBN# 0-9703729-6-5

Note to Teachers:
- Teachers may duplicate pages for classroom use.
- We ask that each individual teacher purchase his or her own copy of the book.
- Schools & teachers may call for group discounts on book purchases.
- Please make reference to the book when using a page with your students.

Thank you!

Other Publications from Missing Piece Press:
Thinklers: A Collection of Brain Ticklers!
State Debate: 50 Unique Playing Cards and 50 Games for Learning about the States!
Number Wonders: A Collection of Amazing Number Facts!
Dreams, Scream, & JellyBeans: Poems for All Ages
The Storybook: A novel for ages 10 on up.
History Mysteries: A New Twist on Timelines – Games & Activities for Learning History.

Missing Piece Press is publisher of educational books and games. Our goal is produce products that fill the user with a sense of fun, wonder, and intrigue.

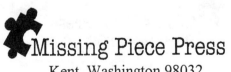
Missing Piece Press
Kent, Washington 98032
Toll Free 1-877-56 THINK
MissingPiecePress.com

Contents

Introduction

"The *WORK* of children is *PLAY*."

We would love to see our children keep physically fit. So, should we get them into a jogging and weight training routine? Or, should we get them involved in playing tag, climbing trees, playing on the monkey bars, swimming, or playing a sport?

The point, of course, is that from a kid's perspective, jogging and weight training are "boring." They are not "fun" and if not perceived as fun they are not going to be motivated to do them. If forced, it will produce results, but not like the results we would see if they were truly *engaged* in the activities.

The same dynamics occur with academic studies and thinking. However, it is a little more challenging to turn what kids are studying or the skills they need to acquire, into an engaging and "fun" activity. But, this is what **Missing Piece Press** is all about.

Founded by a group of teachers who began to realize that though expectations for student achievement were increasing…student motivation and enthusiasm for being at school was not. We realized that what was missing…the *missing piece*, was a **sense** of fun.

Fun, like most things in life, is looked at from many perspectives. What may be fun for one, may be despised by others – there are countless examples. In many schools, fun is a term that is used with great reservation. It can provoke images and thoughts of being frivolous, shallow, or not culturally important. It is true that there are many "fun" toys, games, and activities that truly do not have lasting value or skill development benefits. But, **Missing Piece Press** continues with the belief that "fun" should be a component of the school setting. Our goal is to create, design, and produce products that engage the user in all aspects of learning – knowledge acquisition, various thinking skills, social interaction etc.

We fully understand, and make public claim, that our products are not the panacea for student success. Rather, they are a component that has either been further pushed aside or never was there.

We recall listening to a group of 5th grade students a few years ago when Pokemon cards were at their peak. They were rattling off a slew of information about the characters. When asked how they knew all of this, their reply was "we play with the cards!"

We believe teachers and parents alike do a great job of "teaching" children – giving them knowledge, sharing information, and showing them skills and strategies. What we believe we do not do is give kids enough opportunity or the vehicle for playing with this information. It is through non-threatening playtime that kids (people) can better assimilate what they have learned or are in the process of learning.

Missing Piece Press 2004

Letter From the Author

This is a collection of open ended activities designed to work in the classroom or as independent assignments. Students can work with partners or individually. They can be assigned with time limits or used as ongoing series. I hope that your **students will have fun with words and learn something new** at the same time. Assignments are appropriate for:

Emergent Readers/Writers
Experienced Readers/Writers
Fluent Readers/Writers

Word Chains can be used as a preliminary step towards commercial word games. They are "preloaded" with simple words, and can be used 3-4 at a sitting, using a 6-minute time limit for each puzzle ("How many words can you find in six minutes? GO!) **Word Searches** include several puzzles of "tired word" alternatives. "Tired words" are words used too often in writing, such as "said," "go" and "pretty." Starting with a word search, the word lists used in these puzzles could also be used for activities such as word sorts, alphabetizing, and sentence writing.

There are two sizes of alphabets included, to be used at teacher discretion. The smaller alphabet (found in the Alliteration section) can be used with any **Scavenger Hunt** to create a more formal presentation such as a student created book or report, using the scavenger hunt words as starters for sentences or paragraphs. The larger letters (found in Classroom Helps) could be used to create presentations from the **Alliteration** worksheets, or even as students' initials for personal projects. Also in the Classroom Helps are some suggestions for reading slogans.

I hope you find these activities helpful for meeting the diverse needs of your classroom group.

Sincerely,

Terri Landers

Please note:

- Each section of this book has a code that identifies the appropriate level for the activity presented.

These puzzles are most appropriate for:

Key:

*   Emergent Readers/Writers

**   Experienced Readers/Writers

*** Fluent Readers/Writers

- The following page summarizes these classifications.

Puzzle / Activity Classification

*

Puzzles designed for **Emergent Readers/Writers**:
Word Chains

Phonograms are word patterns. Using a list of 28 phonograms, I have created more than 40 Word Chain puzzles. These phonograms (rimes) can generate more than 600 one-syllable words. Here is a chart, which presents them in rank order determined by the number of words that can be made from the rime and sample words in parentheses:

-ay (say, day)	-ot (pot, hot)	-op (mop, hop)	-ob (job, rob)
-ill (hill, fill)	-ing (wing, ring)	-in (pin, tin)	-ock (dock, clock)
-ip (ship, trip)	-ap (tap, gap)	-an (pan, can)	-ale (pale, tale)
-at (fat, cat)	-unk (junk, skunk)	-est (best, rest)	-ine (line, fine)
-am (jam, ham)	-ail (pail, hail)	-ink (pink, link)	-ight (right, light)
-ag (bag, lag)	-ain (rain, train)	-ow (bow, cow)	-im (him, swim)
-ack (sack, lack)	-eed (seed, reed)	-ew (few, new)	-uck (duck, luck)
-ank (tank, sank)	-y (my, cry)	-ore (core, more)	-um (gum, drum)
-ick (pick, quick)	-out (pout, tout)	-ed (red, bed)	
-ell (tell, fell)	-ug (bug, tug)	-ab (cab, jab)	

Alliteration
Scavenger Hunts
Word Quakes
Word Searches

**

Puzzles appropriate for
Experienced Readers/Writers:

Alliteration
Cryptographs
Homonyms
Idioms
Morphemes
Oxymoron
Scavenger Hunts
Word Chains
Word Quakes
Word Searches
Word Sorts

***

Puzzles appropriate for
Fluent Readers/Writers:

Alliteration
Cryptographs
Homonyms
Idioms
Morphemes
Oxymoron
Scavenger Hunts
Word Chains
Word Quakes
Word Replays (More with Morphemes)
Word Searches
Word Sort
Word Hunt

About the Author

Terri Landers is currently teaching elementary school in Kent, Washington for the Federal Way School District. She has taught fourth, fifth and sixth grades in single and combination classes. Terri received her Masters degree in Curriculum Design and Administration from Gonzaga University.

Cryptography

Secret codes are often used in military operations to prevent the enemy from reading confidential words and sentences. While the information can be sent and received in many different ways, both the sender and the receiver have to recognize and understand the same pattern or "code."

Word Chunking, Vocabulary Expansion

These puzzles are most appropriate for:

✳✳

✳✳✳

Zoo Animals

Using the deciphered word, find the other 'smelly' details. Use the alphabet to finish the key. Then write a sentence about a particular exotic animal *you* like and use the key to write the same sentence in code.

<u>ELEPHANT</u>
1) VOVKSZMG

2) NLMPVB

3) TLIROOZ

4) KVMTFRM

5) YLZ

    XLMHGIRXGLI

6) OVNFI

7) UOZNRMTL

8) SRKKLKLGZNFH

9) TRIZUUV

10) TZAVOOV

11) DLOU

12) IVRMWVVI

13) YFGGVIUOB

14) KLOZI YVZI

15) ORLM

A =
B =
C =
D =
E =
F =
G = T
H =
I =
J =
K = P
L =
M = N
N =
O = L
P =
Q =
R =
S = H
T =
U =
V = E
W =
X =
Y =
Z = A

10

Talent Show

Using the deciphered word, find the other 'entertaining' details. Use the alphabet to finish the key. Then write a sentence about a particular talent you have or like to watch and use the key to write the same sentence in code.

MICROPHONE

1) RJDMPOKPQB

2) YFO CFQDJQL

3) DPRBCJFQ

4) IXLLGBMZ

5) RFLJDJFQ

6) OPODPMQ

7) FOOGFXZB

8) GJLKYZ

9) DFRBMFZ

10) FDYJPQ

11) ZJQLBM

12) MPDH ZYFM

13) FQQPXQDBM

14) XQJDTDGB

15) DXMYFJQ

A =
B = E
C =
D = C
E =
F =
G =
H =
I =
J = I
K = H
L =
M = R
N =
O = P
P = O
Q = N
R = M
S =
T =
U =
V =
W =
X =
Y =
Z =

11

Business Dealings

Using the deciphered word, find the other 'money making' details. Use the alphabet to help finish the key. Then write a sentence about a particular business *you* might try and use the key to write the same sentence in code.

LAWN MOWING

1) ALPY ZXPDYF

2) AHZXYLIH TSLYI

3) GHHIDYF JLST

4) JLU PLTE

5) IXF TELZWXX

6) NLUI TLAH

7) IXF PLABDYF

8) PHHI WRAADYF

9) KLKNTDSSDYG

10) PLTEDYF IDTEHT

11) FLULFH TLAH

12) EXRTH TDSSDYF

13) PLSHUDYF FAXPHUT

14) DSLADLY DJH TSLYI

15) JXZWRSHU AHTTXYT

A = L	
B =	
C =	
D = I	
E =	
F = G	
G =	
H =	
I =	
J =	
K =	
L = A	
M =	
N =	
O =	
P = W	
Q =	
R =	
S =	
T =	
U =	
V =	
W =	
X = O	
Y = N	
Z = M	

Family Pets

Using the deciphered word, find the other 'friendly' details. Use the alphabet to finish the key. Then write a sentence about a particular pet you like and use the key to write the same sentence in code.

<u>PARAKEET</u>

1) ETCTJPPA

2) NPCHTG   BMPEMPCQ

3) NPCSLI

4) MTHBAPC

5) RTGTCV

6) RTILRF   RTA

7) OPCCPA

8) TISLGF   EVAMFG

9) BLTHPBP   RTA

10) MFCBP

11) NFIQOLBM

12) AZCAIP

13) RCLRJPA

14) OCFN

15) SITRJ   ITSCTQFC

A =
B =
C =
D =
E =
F =
G =
H =
I =
J =
K =
L =
M =
N =
O =
P =
Q =
R =
S =
T =
U =
V =
W =
X =
Y =
Z =

Tool Time

Using the deciphered word, find the other 'working' details. Use the alphabet to help finish the key. Then write a sentence about a particular job you like or dislike and use the key to write the same sentence in code.

<u>LAWN   MOWER</u>

1) ALPY   ZXPHU

2) PEHHA   KLUUXP

3) ULBH

4) EXH

5) JADWWHUT

6) PHHI HLSHU

7) PLSHUDYF   EXTH

8) SDAAHU

9) TWUDYBAHU

10) PUHYJE

11) ELZZHU

12) TJUHP   IUDQHU

13) TLP

14) TEXQHA

15) WURYHU

16) GHYJH

A =
B =
C =
D =
E =
F =
G =
H =
I =
J =
K =
L =
M =
N =
O =
P =
Q =
R =
S =
T =
U =
V =
W =
X =
Y =
Z =

14

Orchestral Instruments

Using the deciphered word, find the other 'musical' details. Use the alphabet to finish the key. Then write the name of a favorite musical group and a favorite song and use the key to write them in code.

<u>CLAR INET</u>

1) OZCSUBFN

2) MCLLRRB

3) YCSE

4) EUCBR

5) JURZC

6) QSFBOY YRSB

7) OFZZR

8) AFNNZFISWV

9) MCLL

10) NSWVEFN

11) JURZUB

12) RMRF

13) QZWNF

14) NSRVMRBF

15) LDVEYRBD

16) VWLUO

17) ORBIWONRS

A =
B = N
C = A
D =
E =
F = E
G =
H =
I =
J =
K =
L =
M =
N = T
O = C
P =
Q =
R =
S = R
T =
U = I
V =
W =
X =
Y =
Z = L

Flowers

Using the deciphered word, find the other 'budding' details. Use the alphabet to help finish the key. Then write a sentence about a favorite outdoor activity you like and use the key to write the same sentence in code.

<u>SNAPDRAGON</u>

1) NYDTJODPUY

2) QUYKBNIFWXK

3) JDRNB

4) TKMIYRD

5) EIMMKOFIT

6) NMUFW

7) JDLLUJRX

8) ARYYRD

9) TDYNB

10) HRUXKM

11) RORN

12) PKODYRIZ

13) OUNK

14) TUTTB

A =
B =
C =
D = A
E =
F =
G =
H =
I =
J = D
K =
L =
M =
N = S
O = R
P = G
Q =
R =
S =
T = P
U = O
V =
W =
X =
Y = N
Z =

16

School Time

Using the deciphered word, find the other 'school' trivia words. Use the alphabet to finish the key. Then write the name of your favorite school activity and something you like to do with your friends and use the key to write both in code.

SOC IAL STUD IES
DTQZKX DOVUZLD

OLKQPLJ

DOVULRO

XLKJRZRY QLROLJ

DGLXXZRY

KJZOPELOZQ

JLKUZRY

PTELSTJI

GJZRQZGKX

SJZOZRY

QXKDDJTTE

DQZLRQL

XZFJKJC

DOVUC

A =
B =
C =
D =
E =
F =
G =
H =
I =
J =
K =
L =
M =
N =
O =
P =
Q =
R =
S =
T =
U =
V =
W =
X =
Y =
Z =

Cryptogram Keys

Zoo Animals
elephant
monkey
gorilla
penguin
boa constrictor
lemur
flamingo
hippopotamus
giraffe
gazelle
wolf
reindeer
butterfly
polar bear
lion

Talent Show Key
microphone
tap dancing
comedian
jugglers
magician
popcorn
applause
lights
cameras
action
singer
rock star
announcer
unicycle
curtain

Business Dealings
lawn mowing
lemonade stand
feeding cats
car wash
dog shampoo
yard sale
dog walking
weed pulling
babysitting
washing dishes
garage sale
house sitting
watering flowers
Italian ice stand
computer lessons

Family Pets
calico cat
German Shepherd
gerbil
hamster
canary
parakeet
ferret
albino python
Siamese cat
horse
goldfish
turtle
cricket
frog
Black Labrador

Tool Time
lawn mower
wheel barrow
rake
hoe
clippers
weed eater
watering hose
tiller
sprinkler
wrench
hammer
screw driver
saw
shovel
pruner
fence

Cryptography
If you think you can, or think you can't, you are right.

Orchestral Key
clarinet
bassoon
harp
piano
viola
French horn
cello
kettledrum
bass
trumpet
violin
oboe
flute
trombone
symphony
music
conductor

Flowers
snapdragon
honeysuckle
daisy
petunia
buttercup
stock
daffodil
zinnia
pansy
violet
iris
geranium
rose
poppy

School Time
social studies
teacher
student
learning center
spelling
arithmetic
reading
homework
principal
writing
classroom
science
library
study

Cryptography

Cryptography is the study of secret codes. A specialist in secret codes is called a cryptographer. Here is a secret code that uses symbols other than letters and numbers.

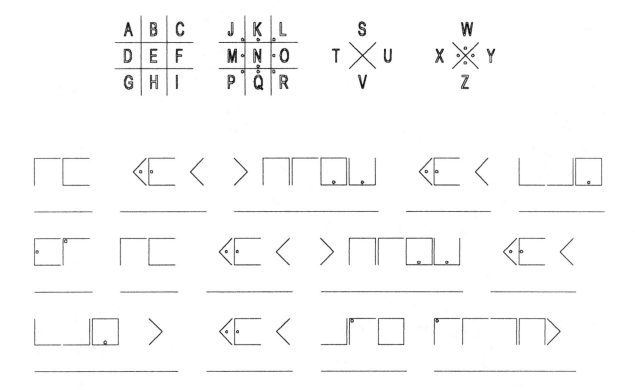

Now, write your name and your favorite book title using the same code down below.

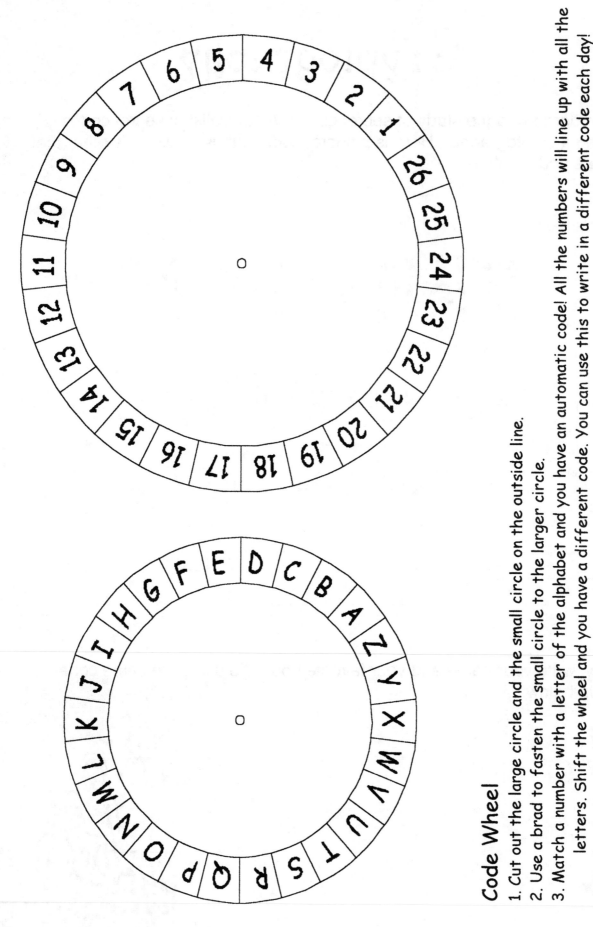

Code Wheel

1. Cut out the large circle and the small circle on the outside line.
2. Use a brad to fasten the small circle to the larger circle.
3. Match a number with a letter of the alphabet and you have an automatic code! All the numbers will line up with all the letters. Shift the wheel and you have a different code. You can use this to write in a different code each day!
4. Write a secret message using one of your new codes.

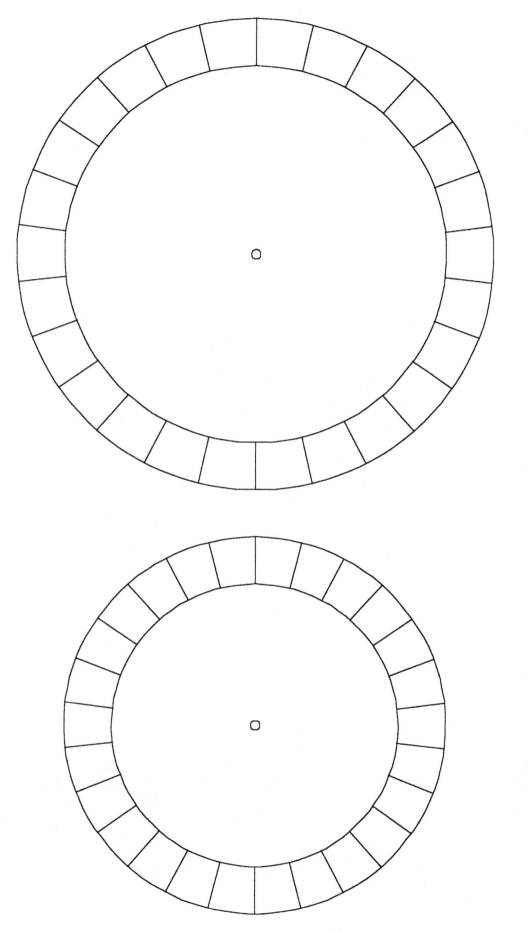

Alternative Code Wheel

Create your own pattern for a code. Use the alphabet backwords or make your own symbols. Use just even numbers, or odd numbers. One wheel will need to have the regular alphabet. Cut out the two wheels on the outside lines and fasten them with a brad. Write a secret message with your new code.

Alliteration

The repetition of sounds.

These puzzles are most appropriate for:

∗
∗∗
∗∗∗

Alliteration repetitions of sounds

Pick a letter .., a personal letter, perhaps the initial of your name, and try to write the longest sentence in which *every* word starts with that letter. The sentence should make sense even if it is not sensible. Example:

NOUN: **dogs**
VERB: **destroy**
NOUN: **dinosaurs**

Now add more describing words that also include the same sound:

Dozens of dangerous dogs destroy ditzy delicious dinosaurs.

Letter:

Noun: _____

Verb: _____

Noun: _____

Extended version:

_____

Now illustrate your new tongue twister:

once more # Alliteration repetitions of sounds

Alliteration is fun to say and enjoyable to hear. Brainstorm nouns, adjectives, adverbs and verbs beginning with a particular letter ("T" for Thanksgiving, "O" for October) and write some tongue twisters.

Letter _____
_____
_____
_____
_____
_____

Letter _____
_____
_____
_____
_____
_____

Letter _____
_____
_____
_____
_____
_____

Letter _____
_____
_____
_____
_____
_____

Letter _____
_____
_____
_____
_____
_____

Letter _____
_____
_____
_____
_____
_____

 **Alliteration** repetitions of sounds

Make up several tongue twisters about popular products you use. Example: *milk, makes, mustaches* **My milk might make messy, milky mustaches.**

Product: _____

Verb: _____

Noun: _____

Now add more describing words that also include the same sound:

Extended version:

_____

- -

Product: _____

Verb: _____

Noun: _____

Extended version:

_____

- -

Product: _____

Verb: _____

Noun: _____

Extended version:

_____

encore Alliteration repetitions of sounds

1. Choose ONE letter of the alphabet.   A B C D E ... _____

2. Brainstorm a list of words beginning with this sound.

   _____   _____   _____

   _____   _____   _____

   _____   _____   _____

   _____   _____   _____

3. Write a verse about an animal whose name begins
   with your chosen letter, using as many words as possible from the
   list.   Bonus: Copy the poem on a large cutout of the letter.

   Animal's Name _____

_____

_____

_____

_____

_____

_____

_____

_____

Alliteration repetitions of sounds

1. Choose ONE letter of the alphabet.   A B C D E ... _____

2. Brainstorm a list of words beginning with this sound.

   _____   _____   _____

   _____   _____   _____

   _____   _____   _____

   _____   _____   _____

3. Write a verse about an imaginary character whose name begins
   with your chosen letter, using as many words as possible from the
   list.   Bonus: Copy the poem on a large cutout of the letter.

   Character's Name _____

   _____

   _____

   _____

   _____

   _____

   _____

   _____

   _____

another ᴀᴌᴌɪᴛᴇʀᴀᴛɪᴏɴ repetitions of sounds

1. Choose ONE letter of the alphabet.   A B C D E ... _____

2. Brainstorm a list of words beginning with this sound.

_____   _____   _____

_____   _____   _____

_____   _____   _____

_____   _____   _____

3. Write a verse about an alien whose name begins
   with your chosen letter, using as many words as possible from the
   list.   Bonus: Copy the poem on a large cutout of the letter.

   Alien's Name _____

_____

_____

_____

_____

_____

_____

_____

_____

and more # Alliteration repetitions of sounds

Start with a particular topic, then brainstorm words that start with the same sound, for instance "w" and "wh" words for the topic "wind".

Topic: _____

Words:

_____   _____   _____
_____   _____   _____
_____   _____   _____
_____   _____   _____

Next, make a mobile using your words and phrases about wind, laughing leaves or penguins carrying their words in a parade.

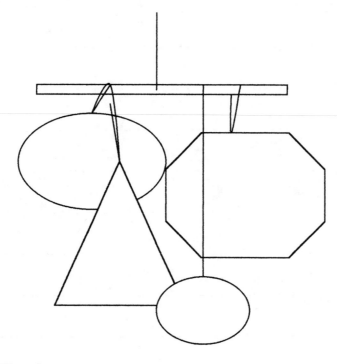

 **Alliteration** repetitions of sounds

Bartholomew Biggins blew big, blue bubbles.

PESTY PETER PIPER PLUCKED PLUMP, PURPLE, PLASTIC PICKLES.

Quinton Quest quite quickly quelled the quarreling quartet.

Xerxes Xenon expected to xerox extra x-rays.

Many monkeys make mud-pies on miserable Monday mornings!

Write more of your own tongue twisters, then choose several to illustrate on separate paper.

_____

_____

_____

_____

_____

_____

_____

Homonyms

Words that sound the same
but are spelled differently
and have different meanings.

These puzzles are most appropriate for:

**

***

Homonym "Pears" #1

Homonyms are words that sound alike but differ in both spelling and meaning. Write down a sentence for each of the words below, using the correct word for the correct meaning. Spelling counts, so use a dictionary! The first two have been done for you.

nay   neigh

1)   "Nay, I won't let down my long hair!" Rapunzel said to the gnome._____

2)   The horse gave a neigh when he saw the carrot._____

none   nun

3)_____

4)_____

or   oar

5)_____

6)_____

oh   owe

7)_____

8)_____

one   won

9)_____

10)_____

plum   plumb

11)_____

12)_____

Homonym "Pears" #2

Homonyms are words that sound alike but differ in both spelling and meaning. Write down a sentence for each of the words below, using the correct word for the correct meaning. Spelling counts, so use a dictionary! The first two have been done for you.

morning   mourning

1) The next morning was the day of the spelling test._____

2) He was mourning for the long empty days of summer._____

mown   moan

3)_____

4)_____

mote   moat

5)_____

6)_____

mode   mowed

7)_____

8)_____

mousse   moose

9)_____

10)_____

mussel   muscle

11)_____

12)_____

Homonym "Pears" #3

Homonyms are words that sound alike but differ in both spelling and meaning. Write down a sentence for each of the words below, using the correct word for the correct meaning. Spelling counts, so use a dictionary! The first two have been done for you.

mustard   mustered

1)__Please pass the mustard to the other end of the table._____

2)__She mustered up the courage to give him the special card._____

peace   piece

3)_____

4)_____

peek   peak

5)_____

6)_____

peal   peel

7)_____

8)_____

pain   pane

9)_____

10)_____

pail   pale

11)_____

12)_____

Homonym "Pears" #4

Homonyms are words that sound alike but differ in both spelling and meaning. Write down a sentence for each of the words below, using the correct word for the correct meaning. Spelling counts, so use a dictionary! The first two have been done for you.

peal   peel

1)   The peal of the bell tore through the air. _____ . _____

2)   He carefully tore the orange peel off in one piece. _____

peddle   pedal

3)_____

4)_____

pare   pear

5)_____

6)_____

palette   palate

7)_____

8)_____

patience   patients

9)_____

10)_____

paws   pause

11)_____

12)_____

Homonym "Pears" #5

Homonyms are words that sound alike but differ in both spelling and meaning. Write down a sentence for each of the words below, using the correct word for the correct meaning. Spelling counts, so use a dictionary!

peer   pier

1)_____

2)_____

pie   pi
3)_____

4)_____

plain   plane
5)_____

6)_____

please   pleas
7)_____

8)_____

plum   plumb
9)_____

10)_____

pole   poll
11)_____

12)_____

Homonym "Pears" #6

Homonyms are words that sound alike but differ in both spelling and meaning. Write down a sentence for each of the words below, using the correct word for the correct meaning. Spelling counts, so use a dictionary!

prophet   profit

1)_____

2)_____

rack   wrack

3)_____

4)_____

reign   rain

5)_____

6)_____

raze   raise

7)_____

8)_____

wrap   rap

9)_____

10)_____

rapt   wrapped

11)_____

12)_____

Homonym "Pears" #7

Homonyms are words that sound alike but differ in both spelling and meaning. Write down a sentence for each of the words below, using the correct word for the correct meaning. Spelling counts, so use a dictionary!

reed   read

1)_____

2)_____

real   reel

3)_____

4)_____

red   read

5)_____

6)_____

review   revue

7)_____

8)_____

row   roe

9)_____

10)_____

rhyme   rime

11)_____

12)_____

Homonym "Pears" #8

Homonyms are words that sound alike but differ in both spelling and meaning. Write down a sentence for each of the words below, using the correct word for the correct meaning. Spelling counts, so use a dictionary!

right   rite

1)_____

2)_____

ring   wring

3)_____

4)_____

role   roll

5)_____

6)_____

wrote   rote

7)_____

8)_____

ruff   rough

9)_____

10)_____

poor   pour

11)_____

12)_____

Hints of Homonyms #1

Homonyms are words that sound alike but differ in both spelling and meaning.
Write a homonym for each word in the space to the right. Spelling counts,
so use a dictionary! The first one has been done for you.

Bonus: Choose ten pairs of words and use each set in ten sentences on the back of this paper.

1. eight   ate
2. all   _____
3. aunt   _____
4. ark   _____
5. aweigh   _____
6. aye   _____
7. bale   _____
8. bawl   _____
9. band   _____
10. bear   _____
11. base   _____
12. bee   _____
13. beech   _____
14. beat   _____
15. beau   _____

16. berth   _____
17. byte   _____
18. blew   _____
19. boar   _____
20. bore   _____
21. board   _____
22. bough   _____
23. break   _____
24. bread   _____
25. bridle   _____
26. buy   _____
27. cache   _____
28. way   _____
29. would   _____
30. yolk   _____

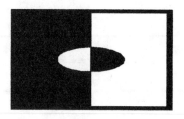

Hints of Homonyms #2

Homonyms are words that sound alike but differ in both spelling and meaning.
Write a homonym for each word in the space to the right. Spelling counts,
so use a dictionary! The first one has been done for you.

Bonus: Choose ten pairs of words and use each set in ten sentences on the back of this paper.

1. capitol   _capital_
2. carat   _____
3. cede   _____
4. cell   _____
5. seller   _____
6. cent   _____
7. sense _____
8. cereal _____
9. choose _____
10. chili _____
11. coral _____
12. shoot _____
13. site _____
14. clause _____
15. clothes _____

16. coarse _____
17. colonel _____
18. corps _____
19. creak _____
20. queue _____
21. symbol _____
22. daze _____
23. dear _____
24. dew _____
25. die _____
26. dough _____
27. urn _____
28. ewe _____
29. fare _____
30. faze _____

43

Hints of Homonyms #3

Homonyms are words that sound alike but differ in both spelling and meaning. Write a homonym for each word in the space to the right. Spelling counts, so use a dictionary! The first one has been done for you.

Bonus: Choose ten pairs of words and use each set in ten sentences on the back of this paper.

1. feat ____feet____

2. fir _____

3. flare _____

4. flee _____

5. flu _____

6. flour _____

7. four _____

8. fowl _____

9. friar _____

10. gait _____

11. gene _____

12. knew _____

13. gourd _____

14. grate _____

15. groan _____

16. hale _____

17. hair _____

18. haul _____

19. hart _____

20. hey _____

21. heal _____

22. here _____

23. heard _____

24. high _____

25. higher _____

26. hymn _____

27. horde _____

28. hoarse _____

29. hose _____

30. our _____

Hints of Homonyms #4

Homonyms are words that sound alike but differ in both spelling and meaning.
Write a homonym for each word in the space to the right. Spelling counts,
so use a dictionary! The first one has been done for you.

Bonus: Choose ten pairs of words and use each set in ten sentences on the back of this paper.

1. hold ___holed___
2. whole _____
3. holey _____
4. idol _____
5. inn _____
6. knap _____
7. kneed _____
8. night _____
9. not _____
10. know _____
11. nose _____
12. leach _____
13. led _____
14. leek _____
15. lien _____

16. lyre _____
17. lie _____
18. lynx _____
19. loan _____
20. lox _____
21. maid _____
22. mail _____
23. mane _____
24. maize _____
25. maul _____
26. marshall _____
27. meat _____
28. medal _____
29. meddle _____
30. mind _____

Hints of Homonyms #5

Homonyms are words that sound alike but differ in both spelling and meaning.
Write a homonym for each word in the space to the right. Spelling counts,
so use a dictionary! The first one has been done for you.

Bonus: Choose ten pairs of words and use each set in ten sentences on the back of this paper.

1. roe _____row_____
2. rime _____
3. right _____
4. wring _____
5. role _____
6. rote _____
7. ruff _____
8. poor _____
9. prays _____
10. prey _____
11. presence _____
12. prints _____
13. principle _____
14. wry _____
15. sail _____

16. scene _____
17. sea _____
18. seam _____
19. seize _____
20. sow _____
21. sheer _____
22. shoo _____
23. sighed _____
24. size _____
25. sign _____
26. sleigh _____
27. slue _____
28. soar _____
29. sword _____
30. sole _____

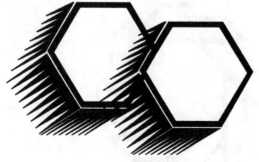

Hints of Homonyms #6

Homonyms are words that sound alike but differ in both spelling and meaning.
Write a homonym for each word in the space to the right. Spelling counts,
so use a dictionary! The first one has been done for you.

Bonus: Choose ten pairs of words and use each set in ten sentences on the back of this paper.

1. new ____gnu____

2. gored _____

3. great _____

4. grown _____

5. hail _____

6. hare _____

7. thyme _____

8. tic _____

9. tied _____

10. too _____

11. towed _____

12. toe _____

13. tuff _____

14. troupe _____

15. vale _____

16. vain _____

17. vial _____

18. whale _____

19. waist _____

20. weight _____

21. war _____

22. ware _____

23. weigh _____

24. yoke _____

25. weak _____

26. whine _____

27. wined _____

28. wood _____

29. sighs _____

30. yore _____

Selected Homonyms

ad	beach	cash	sight	draft
add	beech	capital	site	draught
ade	beat	capitol	clause	earn
aid	beet	carat	claws	urn
ail	beau	carrot	close	ewe
ale	bow	karat	clothes	yew
air	been	cast	coarse	you
ere	bin	caste	course	fair
err	beer	cay	colonel	fare
heir	bier	key	kernel	faze
aisle	berth	quay	complement	phase
isle	birth	cede	compliment	feat
ait	bight	seed	coo	feet
ate	bite	cel	coup	fir
eight	byte	cell	core	fur
all	blew	sell	corps	flair
awl	blue	cellar	creak	flare
ant	bloc	seller	creek	flea
aunt	block	censer	cue	flee
ante	boar	censor	queue	flew
anti	bore	sensor	cygnet	flu
arc	board	cent	signet	flue
ark	bored	scent	cymbal	flocks
away	bode	sent	symbol	phlox
aweigh	bowed	cents	days	flour
aye	bough	sense	daze	flower
eye	bow	cereal		for
bail	brake	serial		fore
bale	break	chased	dear	four
bait	bread	chaste	deer	foreword
bate	bred	chews	defused	forward
ball	bridal	choose	diffused	foul
bawl	bridle	chili	dew	fowl
band	broach	chilly	do	freeze
banned	brooch	choral	due	frieze
bare	but	coral	die	friar
bear	butt	chorale	dye	fryer
base	buy	corral	discreet	gait
bass	by	chute	discrete	gate
be	bye	shoot	doe	gene
bee	cache	cite	dough	jean

48

gild	holed	lye	muscle	pistil
guild	hole	links	mussel	pistol
gnu	whole	lynx	mustard	plain
knew	holey	loan	mustered	plane
new	holy	lone	naval	pleas
gored	wholly	locks	navel	please
gourd	hour	lox	nay	plum
grate	our	made	nee	plumb
great	idle	maid	neigh	pole
grisly	idol	mail	none	poll
grizzly	ileum	male	nun	poor
groan	ilium	main	oar	pore
grown	in	mane	or	pour
hail	inn	maize	ore	praise
hale	knap	maze	oh	prays
hair	nap	mall	owe	pray
hare	knead	maul	one	prey
hall	kneed	marshall	won	presence
haul	need	martial	pail	presents
halve	knight	mean	pale	prince
have	night	mien	pain	prints
hart	knit	meat	pane	principal
heart	nit	meet	pair	principle
hay	knot	mete	pare	profit
hey	not	medal	pear	prophet
heal	know	meddle	palate	psalter
heel	no	might	palette	salter
hear	knows	mite	patience	sigh
here	nose	mince	patients	rack
heard	lay	mints	pause	wrack
herd	lei	mind	paws	rain
heroin	lays	mined	peace	reign
heroine	laze	moan	piece	rein
hi	leas	mown	peak	raise
high	leis	moat	peek	rays
higher	leach	mote	pique	raze
hire	leech	mode	peal	rap
him	lead	mowed	peel	wrap
hymn	led	moo	pearl	rapt
hoard	leak	moue	perl	wrapped
horde	leek	moor	pedal	read
hoarse	lean	more	peddle	reed
horse	lien	moose	peer	read
hoes	liar	mousse	pier	red
hose	lyre	morning	pi	real
hold	lie	mourning	pie	reel

reek	sheik	sweet	veil
wreak	shear	tacks	vain
rest	sheer	tax	vane
wrest	shoe	tail	vial
retch	shoo	tale	vile
wretch	shore	tare	wail
review	sure	tear	whale
revue	side	taught	waist
rho	sighed	taut	waste
roe	sighs	tea	wait
row	size	tee	weight
rhyme	sign	team	want
rime	sine	teem	wont
right	slay	tear	war
rite	sleigh	tier	wore
wright	sleight	tease	ware
write	slight	tees	wear
ring	slew	tense	where
wring	slue	tents	way
role	sloe	tern	weigh
roll	slow	turn	we
root	soar	their	wee
route	sore	there	weak
rote	soared	threw	week
wrote	sword	through	whine
rough	sole	throne	wine
ruff	soul	thrown	why
rout	some	thyme	wye
route	sum	time	wind
rye	son	tic	wined
wry	sun	tick	wood
sail	spade	tide	would
sale	spayed	tied	yoke
scene	staid	to	yolk
seen	stayed	too	yore
sea	stair	two	your
see	stare	toad	
seam	stake	towed	
seem	steak	toe	
seas	stationary	tow	
sees	stationery	tough	
seize	steal	tuff	
sew	steel	troop	
so	straight	troupe	
sow	strait	vail	
shake	suite	vale	

 idioms

An idiom is a group of words which, when used together, have a different meaning from the one which the individual words have. For example:
- How do you know about Mary's new job?
- Oh, I heard it **through the grapevine**.

These puzzles are most appropriate for:

*
**
***

Intro to Idioms 1

An idiom is a phrase that has a different meaning than the individual words contained in the phrase. Draw a picture of the underlined words, then use the idiom in a relevant and practical sentence to remember its meaning easily.

<u>raining cats and dogs</u>
means: a lot of rain

<u>change your mind</u>
means: have a new opinion

Intro to Idioms 2

An idiom is a phrase that has a different meaning than the individual words contained *IN* the phrase. Draw a picture of the underlined words, then use the idiom in a relevant and practical sentence to remember its meaning easily.

<u>Cut it out!</u>
means: stop

<u>junk mail</u>
means: unwanted mail

Intro to Idioms 1

An idiom is a phrase that has a different meaning than the individual words contained **IN** the phrase. Draw a picture of the underlined words, then use the idiom in a relevant and practical sentence to remember its meaning easily.

<u>raining cats and dogs</u>
means: a lot of rain

_____

_____

<u>change your mind</u>
means: have a new opinion

_____

_____

Intro to Idioms 3

An idiom is a phrase that has a different meaning than the individual words contained **IN** the phrase. Draw a picture of the underlined words, then use the idiom in a relevant and practical sentence to remember its meaning easily.

<u>two-faced</u>
means: traitor, spy

_____

_____

<u>zip your lip</u>
means: quiet

_____

_____

Intro to Idioms 4

An idiom is a phrase that has a different meaning than the individual words contained *IN* the phrase. Draw a picture of the underlined words, then use the idiom in a relevant and practical sentence to remember its meaning easily.

<u>step on it</u>
means: go fast

<u>pulling your leg</u>
means: just joking

Intro to Idioms 5

An idiom is a phrase that has a different meaning than the individual words contained **IN** the phrase. Draw a picture of the underlined words, then use the idiom in a relevant and practical sentence to remember its meaning easily.

<u>let sleeping dogs lie</u>
means: don't change anything

_____

_____

<u>keep an eye out for</u>
means: look

_____

_____

Intro to Idioms 6

An idiom is a phrase that has a different meaning than the individual words contained **IN** the phrase. Draw a picture of the underlined words, then use the idiom in a relevant and practical sentence to remember its meaning easily.

<u>in over your head</u>
means: won't be able to do

_____

_____

<u>give me a hand</u>
means: help out

_____

_____

Intro to Idioms 7

An idiom is a phrase that has a different meaning than the individual words contained **IN** the phrase. Draw a picture of the underlined words, then use the idiom in a relevant and practical sentence to remember its meaning easily.

<u>fire someone</u>
means: take away the job

_____

_____

<u>elbow grease</u>
means: effort, push

_____

_____

Intro to Idioms 8

An idiom is a phrase that has a different meaning than the individual words contained **IN** the phrase. Draw a picture of the underlined words, then use the idiom in a relevant and practical sentence to remember its meaning easily.

<u>down in the dumps</u>
means: unhappy

_____

_____

<u>cool</u>
means: good idea

_____

_____

Intro to Idioms 9

An idiom is a phrase that has a different meaning than the individual words contained **IN** the phrase. Draw a picture of the underlined words, then use the idiom in a relevant and practical sentence to remember its meaning easily.

<u>break a leg</u>
means: do a good job

_____

_____

<u>beat around the bush</u>
means: avoid the real topic

_____

_____

Intro to Idioms 10

An idiom is a phrase that has a different meaning than the individual words contained *IN* the phrase. Draw a picture of the underlined words, then use the idiom in a relevant and practical sentence to remember its meaning easily.

<u>chow down</u>
means: eat

<u>eager beaver</u>
means: energetic

Intro to Idioms 11

An idiom is a phrase that has a different meaning than the individual words contained **IN** the phrase. Draw a picture of the underlined words, then use the idiom in a relevant and practical sentence to remember its meaning easily.

<u>couch potato</u>
means: inactive person

_____

_____

<u>get a kick out of something</u>
means: enjoy it

_____

_____

Intro to Idioms 12

An idiom is a phrase that has a different meaning than the individual words contained **IN** the phrase. Draw a picture of the underlined words, then use the idiom in a relevant and practical sentence to remember its meaning easily.

<u>change of heart</u>
means: new opinion

_____

_____

<u>hit the books</u>
means: study

_____

_____

Inane Idioms 13

An idiom is a phrase that has a different meaning than the individual words contained *IN* the phrase. Draw a picture of the underlined words, then use the idiom in a relevant and practical sentence to remember its meaning easily.

<u>hit the hay</u>
means: go to bed

<u>inside out</u>
means: turned around

Intro to Idioms 14

An idiom is a phrase that has a different meaning than the individual words contained **IN** the phrase. Draw a picture of the underlined words, then use the idiom in a relevant and practical sentence to remember its meaning easily.

<u>jump the gun</u>
means: start too soon

_____

_____

<u>keep in touch</u>
means: communicate

_____

_____

Intro to Idioms 15

An idiom is a phrase that has a different meaning than the individual words contained *IN* the phrase. Draw a picture of the underlined words, then use the idiom in a relevant and practical sentence to remember its meaning easily.

<u>quite a few</u>
means: a lot

<u>rub someone the wrong way</u>
means: uncomfortable

Idioms

Make an alphabet book by choosing one idiom for each letter of the alphabet. Write the letter, the phrase and create an illustration for each phrase, and write a practical sentence including the phrase on each page. Have fun!

A

ace (verb)
after one's own heart
alley cat
antsy
as easy as pie
at heart

B

badger someone
bark up the wrong tree
bark is worse than his bite
a piece of cake
be all ears
be on the go
be on the road
be up and running
be used to
beat around the bush
Beats me.
bent out of shape
before long
bite off more than one can chew
blabbermouth
black and white
black out
black sheep
blow one's top
blue in the face
boom box
the bottom line
Break a leg!
break someone's heart
broke
brown bag it
bug (verb)
bull-headed
bull in a china shop

C

call it a day
cast pearls before swine
cat get one's tongue
cat nap
catch one's eye
catch someone red-handed
catch some Zs
can't make heads or tails of something
change one's mind
change of heart
chicken
chow
chow down
a cinch
cool (adj.)
copycat
cost (someone) an arm and a leg
couch potato
cram
crash course
cry wolf
curiosity killed the cat
Cut it out!

D

dead duck
dicey
ditch class
Don't count your chickens until they hatch.
do a bang-up job
down in the dumps
dumb bunny
drag one's feet
drop someone a line

E

an eager beaver
easy does it
eat crow
eat like a bird
eat like a horse
eat one's heart out
an egghead
elbow grease

F

far-fetched
fed up
feel blue
fender-bender
fire someone
for ages
for the birds
from the bottom of one's heart
from the heart

G

get going
get it
get a kick out of something
get on one's nerves
get one's wires crossed
get out of hand
get to the heart of things
get up and go
give someone a hand
give someone the green light
go with the flow
grab a bite
grass is always greener on the other side
of the fence
green
green belt
green thumb
green with envy

H

hard feelings
hassle
have one's hands full
have something down pat
head honcho
heard it on the grapevine
heart goes out to
heart is in the right place
heart of gold
heart of stone
heart skips a beat
heart stands still
heart to heart
heavy heart
hit the books
hit the bulls-eye
hit the hay
hit the sack
hold one's horses
holy cow
horse around
horse of a different color
horse sense
horse trade

I

in a pig's eye
if I had my druthers
in over one's head
in the doghouse
inside out
in stock
in the black
in the red
in time

J

jump all over someone
jump the gun
jump to conclusion
junk mail

K

kangaroo court
keep an eye on
keep an eye out for
keep one's chin up
keep one's fingers crossed
keep one's nose to the grindstone
keep (stay) in touch
kid
kind of
a klutz
a know-it-all
know something backwards and forward
know something inside out

L

let-down
lend someone a hand
leave well enough alone
Let sleeping dogs lie.
let the cat out of the bag
like water off of a duck's back
live from hand to mouth
live high on the hog
Live and let live.
lock the barn door after the horse is gone
look a gift horse in the mouth
look at the world with rose-colored
glasses
look like the cat that swallowed the
canary
lose heart
lose track of
a low blow
lousy

M

macho
mad as a hornet
make a mountain out of a mole hill
monkey business
can't make heads or tails of it
make up one's mind

N

nail down
name is mud
name of the game
narrow escape
nick in time
No way!
Not on your life!
now and then
nuts

O

off-color
on the cutting edge
on the dot
on time
once in a while
once in a blue moon
open one's heart
out of the blue
over one's head

P

paint the town red
pay the piper
pecking order
piggyback
piggy bank
pink slip
plastic
play cat and mouse
pop quiz
pot calling the kettle black
pretty (adv.)
pull an all-nighter
pull someone's leg
put the cart before the horse

Q

quite a few
a quick study
John Q. Public

R

rat out on someone
rat race
rain or shine
rain cats and dogs
read someone's mind
red herring
red-letter day
red tape
road hog
roll out the red carpet
rub someone the wrong way
run-down

S

search one's heart/soul
see red
set one's heart on
sitting duck
sleep on it
smell a rat
sooner or later
shoot the breeze
show one's true colors
a snap
no spring chicken
straight from the horse's mouth
state of the art
straw that broke the camel's back
stay in touch
Step on it!

T

take heart
take it easy
take the bull by the horns
tell a white lie
tickled pink
tight-fisted
a tightwad
tough
tricky
two-faced

U

ugly duckling
under the weather
until hell freezes over
until you're blue in the face
upside down
up-to-date
used to

V

virtual reality
face value

W

wear out one's welcome
wear one's heart on one's sleeve
wet behind the ears
What's up?
white elephant
white lie
white sale
with all one's heart
with bells on
with flying colors
wolf in sheep's clothing

X

eXtra-terrestrial
range from X to y

Y

yellow-bellied
yellow streak
a yes-man
You don't say!
You've got to be kidding!
Yucky
yummy

Z

zilch
Zip your lip!

Morphemes

The study of the architecture of words.

aqua	*water*	fract	*break*
agri	*field*	liber	*free*
amphi	*both, around*	loc	*place*
auto	*self*	max	*greatest*
bio	*life*	mono	*single, one*
geo	*earth*	ped	*foot*
graph	*something written*	vis	*see*
cent	*hundred*	tact	*touch*
cogn	*know*	terra	*land*
cine	*movement*	therm	*heat*

oct	*eight*	ology	*study of*
tri	*three*	meter	*measure*
tex	*weave*	onym	*name, word*
nav	*ship*	tele	*far away*
phone	*sound*	port	*carry*
scribe	*write*	photo	*light*
morph	*change*		

These puzzles are most appropriate for:

✱✱
✱✱✱

...emes: aqua geo fract ped oct

define it and list as many words as possible that
...e that word chunk. Write the definition of each

Root _aqua_

Means _water_

Picture of root:

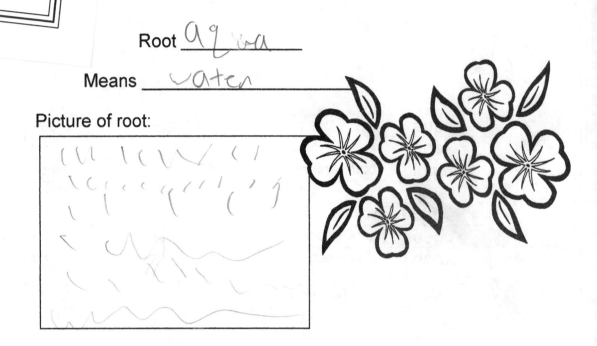

Word	Definition	Word	Definition
aa·ua natur			
a·d har·I· um			
aq·ua for· tis			
aqua re· gi·a			

aqua *water* **geo** *earth* **fract** *break* **ped** *foot* **oct** *eight*

Morphemes: morph photo tri vis liber

Select a morpheme, define it and list as many words as possible that you can find that use that word chunk. Write the definition of each word.

Root _____

Means _____

Picture of root:

Word	Definition		Word	Definition

morph *change*   photo *light*   tri *three*   vis *see*   liber *free*

Morphemes: agri graph terra nav port

Select a morpheme, define it and list as many words as possible that you can find that use that word chunk. Write the definition of each word.

Root _____

Means _____

Picture of root:

Word	Definition		Word	Definition

agri *field*   graph *something written*   terra *land*   nav *ship*   port *carry*

Morphemes: bio cine mono therm phone

Select a morpheme, define it and list as many words as possible that you can find that use that word chunk. Write the definition of each word.

Root _____

Means _____

Picture of root:

Word	Definition		Word	Definition

bio *life*   cine *movement*   mono *single, one*   therm *heat* phone *sound*

Morphemes: cent loc tact cogn max

Select a morpheme, define it and list as many words as possible that you can find that use that word chunk. Write the definition of each word.

Root _____

Means _____

Picture of root:

Word	Definition		Word	Definition

cent *hundred*   loc *place*   tact *touch*   cogn *know*   max *greatest*

Morphemes: tele scribe tex auto amphi

Select a morpheme, define it and list as many words as possible that you can find that use that word chunk. Write the definition of each word.

Root _____

Means _____

Picture of root:

Word	Definition	Word	Definition

tele *far away* scribe *write* tex *weave* auto *self* amphi *both, around*

Word Replay 1

The words below can be sorted into three categories. Can you figure out how to group them?

portal	gradually	digress	retrogress
graduation	regressive	deport	progressive
congressman	imported	transgression	export
support	portable	centigrade	gradient
degradation	aggression	congress	transport

Label each category.

gress		
Explain:		small steps, little by little

Word Replay 2

The words below can be sorted into three categories. Can you figure out how to group them?

motion	exceptional	demotion	contradict
dictionary	verdict	inception	intercept
reception	emotional	dictate	conception
motorcade	benediction	predicament	momentum
acceptance	removal	promotion	addicted

Label each category.

dict		
Explain:	take, get	

Word Replay 3

The words below can be sorted into three categories. Can you figure out how to group them?

spectacular	respect	cadaver	spectrum
casualty	cadence	spectator	occidental
deciduous	suspects	incident	decadent
inspection	coincidence	occasional	inspection
cascade	accidentally	spectacle	prospects

Label each category.

cid		
Explain: **fall, sink**		

Word Replay 4

The words below can be sorted into three categories. Can you figure out how to group them?

vertical	dismissal	establish	standard
revert	advertisement	missionary	omission
circumstance	distance	universal	diversify
conversation	inadmissible	vertical	emission
constant	anniversary	stamina	versatility

Label each category.

miss		
Explain:		stand

Word Replay 5

The words below can be sorted into three categories. Can you figure out how to group them?

quarter	irregular	position	reign
correction	compose	quadrant	squadron
erect	square	composition	posture
quarry	rectangular	quart	realm
composure	regulations	quadrille	proposition

Label each category.

reg		
Explain:		to place

Word Replay 1 Key
gress port grad

gress, grad = little by little, small steps
port = to carry

Word Replay 2 Key
dict cept mot

dict = speak, declare
cept = take, get
mot = move

Word Replay 3 Key
cid   cad   spect

cid = fall, sink
cad = fall, come to an end
spect = see, view

Word Replay 4 Key
sta   miss vert

sta = stand
miss = send
vert = turn

Word Replay 5 Key
reg   quar pos

reg = straight, rule
quar = four
pos = to place

Morphemes: logy meter onym

Select 3 morphemes, define them and list as many words as possible that you can find using that word chunk. Write the definition of each word.

Root: logy	Means: study of
Word	**Definition**
geology	**study of the physical earth**

Root:	Means:
Word	**Definition**

Root:	Means:
Word	**Definition**

ology *study of*   meter *measure*   onym *name, word*

Morphemes: agri graph terra nav port

Select 3 morphemes, define them and list as many words as possible that you can find using that word chunk. Write the definition of each word.

Root: port	Means: carry, move
Word	**Definition**
portable	**easily carried**

Root:	Means:
Word	**Definition**

Root:	Means:
Word	**Definition**

agri *field*   graph *something written*   terra *land*   nav *ship*   port *carry*

Morphemes: bio cine mono therm phone

Select 3 morphemes, define them and list as many words as possible that you can find using that word chunk. Write the definition of each word.

Root: therm	Means: heat
Word	Definition
thermometer	device that measures temperature

Root:	Means:
Word	Definition

Root:	Means:
Word	Definition

bio *life*   cine *movement*   mono *single, one*   therm *heat*   phone *sound*

Morphemes: cent loc tact cogn max

Select 3 morphemes, define them and list as many words as possible that you can find using that word chunk. Write the definition of each word.

Root: cent	Means: hundred
Word	Definition
percent	number of hundredths

Root:	Means:
Word	Definition

Root:	Means:
Word	Definition

cent *hundred* loc *place* tact *touch* cogn *know* max *greatest*

Morphemes: tele scribe tex auto amphi

Select 3 morphemes, define them and list as many words as possible that you can find using that word chunk. Write the definition of each word.

Root: scribe	*Means:* write
Word	**Definition**
transcribe	**write down, copy**

Root:	*Means:*
Word	**Definition**

Root:	*Means:*
Word	**Definition**

tele *far away*   scribe *write*   tex *weave*   auto *self*   amphi *both, around*

Morphemes: aqua geo fract ped oct

Select 3 morphemes, define them and list as many words as possible that you can find using that word chunk. Write the definition of each word.

Root: geo	Means: earth
Word	Definition
geography	study of the world

Root:	Means:
Word	Definition

Root:	Means:
Word	Definition

aqua *water*   geo *earth*   fract *break*   ped *foot*   oct *eight*

Morphemes: morph photo tri vis liber

Select 3 morphemes, define them and list as many words as possible that you can find using that word chunk. Write the definition of each word.

Root: tri	*Means:* three
Word	**Definition**
triangle	**three sided figure**

Root:	*Means:*
Word	**Definition**

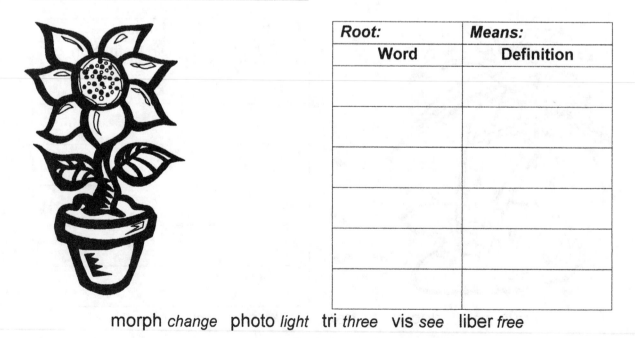

Root:	*Means:*
Word	**Definition**

morph *change*   photo *light*   tri *three*   vis *see*   liber *free*

Oxymorons

putting two contradictory words together.

ox-y-mo'-ron   from Gk. *oxy*, "sharp" and *moros*, "dull"

Self-contradictory word or phrase: **jumbo shrimp**.

When used as a metaphor, it is an insulting means of referring to the physique of someone.

These puzzles are most appropriate for:

✳✳

✳✳✳

Oxymorons 1

putting two contradictory words together

ox-y-mo'-ron   from Gk. *oxy*, "sharp" and *moros*, "dull"

Look at the eight phrases below and choose three to explain why they fit the definition of "oxymoron". Then design a T-shirt logo on the back of this paper using any oxymoron.

act naturally	found missing	resident alien	genuine imitation
good grief	same difference	almost exactly	small crowd

1) phrase:_____

_____

_____

_____

_____

2) phrase:_____

_____

_____

_____

_____

3) phrase:_____

_____

_____

_____

_____

Oxymorons 2

putting two contradictory words together

ox-y-mo'-ron   from Gk. *oxy*, "sharp" and *moros*, "dull"

Look at the phrases below and choose three to explain why they fit the definition of "oxymoron". Then design a T-shirt logo on the back of this paper using any oxymoron.

new classic   *sweet sorrow*   *childproof*   *"now, then ..."*
synthetic natural gas   *passive aggression*   *taped live*

1) phrase:_____

_____

_____

_____

_____

2) phrase:_____

_____

_____

_____

_____

3) phrase:_____

_____

_____

_____

_____

Oxymorons 3

putting two contradictory words together

ox-y-mo'-ron   from Gk. *oxy*, "sharp" and *moros*, "dull"

Look at the six phrases below and choose three to explain why they fit the definition of "oxymoron". Then design a T-shirt logo on the back of this paper using any oxymoron.

pretty ugly   **twelve-ounce pound cake**   **diet ice cream**
working vacation   **exact estimate**   **religious tolerance**

1) phrase:_____

_____

_____

_____

_____

2) phrase:_____

_____

_____

_____

_____

3) phrase:_____

_____

_____

_____

_____

Oxymorons 4

putting two contradictory words together

ox-y-mo'-ron   from Gk. *oxy*, "sharp" and *moros*, "dull"

Look at the phrases below and choose three to explain why they fit
the definition of "oxymoron". Then design a T-shirt logo on the back
of this paper using any oxymoron.

sanitary landfill   *alone together*   *government organization*

silent scream   *living dead*   *business ethics*   *soft rock*

military intelligence   *software documentation*

1) phrase:_____

_____

_____

_____

_____

2) phrase:_____

_____

_____

_____

_____

3) phrase:_____

_____

_____

_____

_____

Oxymorons 5

putting two contradictory words together

ox-y-mo'-ron   from Gk. *oxy*, "sharp" and *moros*, "dull"

Look at the ten phrases below and choose three to explain why they fit the definition of "oxymoron". Then design a T-shirt logo on the back of this paper using any oxymoron.

clearly misunderstood   peace force   extinct life   computer jock
plastic glasses   jumbo shrimp   terribly pleased   political science
tight slacks   definite maybe

1) phrase:_____

_____

_____

_____

_____

2) phrase:_____

_____

_____

_____

_____

3) phrase:_____

_____

_____

_____

_____

Oxymorons 6

putting two contradictory words together

ox-y-mo'-ron   from Gk. *oxy*, "sharp" and *moros*, "dull"

Look at the phrases below and choose three to explain why they fit the definition of "oxymoron". Then design a T-shirt logo on the back of this paper using any oxymoron.

act naturally   adult children   agree to disagree   anxious patient
(almost done, almost exactly, almost ready)   baby grand
bad health   bad luck   black light   awfully good

1) phrase:_____

_____

_____

_____

_____

2) phrase:_____

_____

_____

_____

_____

3) phrase:_____

_____

_____

_____

_____

Scavenger Hunts

Vocabulary Expanders

These puzzles are most appropriate for:

✳
✳✳
✳✳✳

Adverb Scavenger Hunt

In this challenging game, you need to find words or phrases that begin with the given letters. Twenty points for each word.

The category this round: **Adverbs: Words that modify verbs or nouns.**

A _____

B _____

C _____

D _____

E _____

F _____

G _____

H _____

I _____

J _____

K _____

L _____

M _____

N _____

O _____

P _____

Q _____

R _____

S _____

T _____

U _____

V _____

W _____

X _____

Y _____

Z _____

Animal Scavenger Hunt

In this game, you need to find words that begin with the given letters. Ten points for each word, with double points for words that begin with "q" or "x". The category for this round: TYPES OF ANIMALS.

A _____   N _____

B _____   O _____

C _____   P _____

D _____   Q _____

E _____   R _____

F _____   S _____

G _____   T _____

H _____   U _____

I _____   V _____

J _____   W _____

K _____   X _____

L _____   Y _____

M _____   Z _____

Articulate Scavenger Hunt

In this game, you need to find words or phrases that begin with the given letters. Three points for each word, with double points for words or phrases that begin with "q" or "x". The category for this round: **Adjectives: DESCRIBING WORDS.**

A _____ _____ _____ _____

B _____ _____ _____ _____

C _____ _____ _____ _____

D _____ _____ _____ _____

E _____ _____ _____ _____

F _____ _____ _____ _____

G _____ _____ _____ _____

H _____ _____ _____ _____

I _____ _____ _____ _____

J _____ _____ _____ _____

K _____ _____ _____ _____

L _____ _____ _____ _____

M _____ _____ _____ _____

N _____ _____ _____ _____

O _____ _____ _____ _____

P _____ _____ _____ _____

Q _____ _____ _____ _____

R _____ _____ _____ _____

S _____ _____ _____ _____

T _____ _____ _____ _____

U _____ _____ _____ _____

V _____ _____ _____ _____

W _____ _____ _____ _____

X _____ _____ _____ _____

Y _____ _____ _____ _____

Z _____ _____ _____ _____

Athletic Scavenger Hunt

In this game, you need to find words or phrases that begin with the given letters. Ten points for each word or phrase, with double points for terms that begin with "q" or "x". The category for this round: SPORTS AND SPORTS EQUIPMENT.

A _____ _____ _____   N _____ _____ _____

B _____ _____ _____   O _____ _____ _____

C _____ _____ _____   P _____ _____ _____

D _____ _____ _____   Q _____ _____ _____

E _____ _____ _____   R _____ _____ _____

F _____ _____ _____   S _____ _____ _____

G _____ _____ _____   T _____ _____ _____

H _____ _____ _____   U _____ _____ _____

I _____ _____ _____   V _____ _____ _____

J _____ _____ _____   W _____ _____ _____

K _____ _____ _____   X _____ _____ _____

L _____ _____ _____   Y _____ _____ _____

M _____ _____ _____   Z _____ _____ _____

Astronomical Scavenger Hunt

In this game, you need to find words or phrases that begin with the given letters. Ten points for each word or phrase, with double points for items that begin with "q" or "x". The category for this round: THINGS TO DO WITH OUTER SPACE.

A ___ ___ ___   N ___ ___ ___

B ___ ___ ___   O ___ ___ ___

C ___ ___ ___   P ___ ___ ___

D ___ ___ ___   Q ___ ___ ___

E ___ ___ ___   R ___ ___ ___

F ___ ___ ___   S ___ ___ ___

G ___ ___ ___   T ___ ___ ___

H ___ ___ ___   U ___ ___ ___

I ___ ___ ___   V ___ ___ ___

J ___ ___ ___   W ___ ___ ___

K ___ ___ ___   X ___ ___ ___

L ___ ___ ___   Y ___ ___ ___

M ___ ___ ___   Z ___ ___ ___

AUTUMN Scavenger Hunt

In this game, you need to find words that begin with the given letters. Ten points for each word, with double points for words that begin with "q" or "x", 25 points for phrases. The category for this round: THINGS YOU SEE IN FALL.

A _____

B _____

C _____

D _____

E _____

F _____

G _____

H _____

I _____

J _____

K _____

L _____

M _____

N _____

O _____

P _____

Q _____

R _____

S _____

T _____

U _____

V _____

W _____

X _____

Y _____

Z _____

Colorful Scavenger Hunt

In this game, you need to find words or phrases that begin with the given letters. Ten points for each word or phrase, with double points for words that begin with "q" or "x". The category for this round: *CONSPICUOUS COLORS*.

A _____   N _____

B _____   O _____

C _____   P _____

D _____   Q _____

E _____   R _____

F _____   S _____

G _____   T _____

H _____   U _____

I _____   V _____

J _____   W _____

K _____   X _____

L _____   Y _____

M _____   Z _____

Cultural Scavenger Hunt

In this game, you need to find words or phrases that begin with the given letters. Twenty points for each word or phrase, with double points for items that begin with "q" or "x". The category for this round: FACTS ABOUT A COUNTRY

Name of country: _____

A _____   N _____

B _____   O _____

C _____   P _____

D _____   Q _____

E _____   R _____

F _____   S _____

G _____   T _____

H _____   U _____

I _____   V _____

J _____   W _____

K _____   X _____

L _____   Y _____

M _____   Z _____

Flowery Scavenger Hunt

In this game, you need to find words that begin with the given letters. Five points for each name, with double points for names that begin with "q" or "x". The category for this round: TYPES OF FLOWERS.

A _____

B _____

C _____

D _____

E _____

F _____

G _____

H _____

I _____

J _____

K _____

L _____

M _____

N _____

O _____

P _____

Q _____

R _____

S _____

T _____

U _____

V _____

W _____

X _____

Y _____

Z _____

Fossil Scavenger Hunt

In this game, you need to find words that begin with the given letters. Twenty points for each name, with double points for names that begin with "q" or "x". The category for this round: NAMES OF DIFFERENT DINOSAURS.

A _____

B _____

C _____

D _____

E _____

F _____

G _____

H _____

I _____

J _____

K _____

L _____

M _____

N _____

O _____

P _____

Q _____

R _____

S _____

T _____

U _____

V _____

W _____

X _____

Y _____

Z _____

Frosty Fiesta Scavenger Hunt

In this game, you need to find words or phrases that begin with the given letters. Ten points for each word or phrase, with double points for items that begin with "q" or "x". The category for this round: **THINGS TO DO ON A SNOWY DAY.**

A _____   N _____

B _____   O _____

C _____   P _____

D _____   Q _____

E _____   R _____

F _____   S _____

G _____   T _____

H _____   U _____

I _____   V _____

J _____   W _____

K _____   X _____

L _____   Y _____

M _____   Z _____

Global Scavenger Hunt

In this game, you need to find names that begin with the given letters. Twenty points for each word or phrase, with double points for items that begin with "q" or "x". The category for this round: NAMES OF FOREIGN COUNTRIES.

A _____   N _____

B _____   O _____

C _____   P _____

D _____   Q _____

E _____   R _____

F _____   S _____

G _____   T _____

H _____   U _____

I _____   V _____

J _____   W _____

K _____   X _____

L _____   Y _____

M _____   Z _____

Hero Scavenger Hunt

In this game, you need to find names that begin with the given letters. Ten points for each name, with double points for any that begin with "q" or "x". The category for this round: CHARACTERS FOUND IN BOOKS.

A _____   N _____

B _____   O _____

C _____   P _____

D _____   Q _____

E _____   R _____

F _____   S _____

G _____   T _____

H _____   U _____

I _____   V _____

J _____   W _____

K _____   X _____

L _____   Y _____

M _____   Z _____

Literary List Scavenger Hunt

In this game, you need to find titles that begin with the given letters. Twenty points for each title, with double points for titles that begin with "q" or "x". The category for this round: VARIOUS BOOK TITLES.

A _____   N _____

B _____   O _____

C _____   P _____

D _____   Q _____

E _____   R _____

F _____   S _____

G _____   T _____

H _____   U _____

I _____   V _____

J _____   W _____

K _____   X _____

L _____   Y _____

M _____   Z _____

Mathematical Scavenger Hunt

In this game, you need to find words that begin with the given letters. Ten points for each word, with double points for words that begin with "q" or "x". The category for this round: MATH TERMS.

A _____   N _____
B _____   O _____
C _____   P _____
D _____   Q _____
E _____   R _____
F _____   S _____
G _____   T _____
H _____   U _____
I _____   V _____
J _____   W _____
K _____   X _____
L _____   Y _____
M _____   Z _____

My Book Scavenger Hunt

In this game, you need to find words or phrases that begin with the given letters. Ten points for each term, with double points for items that begin with "q" or "x". The category for this round: THINGS ABOUT MY BOOK.

BOOK TITLE _____

A _____   N _____

B _____   O _____

C _____   P _____

D _____   Q _____

E _____   R _____

F _____   S _____

G _____   T _____

H _____   U _____

I _____   V _____

J _____   W _____

K _____   X _____

L _____   Y _____

M _____   Z _____

Noun Scavenger Hunt

In this game, you need to find words or phrases that begin with the given letters. Three points for each word, with double points for words or phrases that begin with "q" or "x". The category: Nouns: PEOPLE, PLACES, THINGS OR GROUPS.

A ___ ___ ___   N ___ ___ ___

B ___ ___ ___   O ___ ___ ___

C ___ ___ ___   P ___ ___ ___

D ___ ___ ___   Q ___ ___ ___

E ___ ___ ___   R ___ ___ ___

F ___ ___ ___   S ___ ___ ___

G ___ ___ ___   T ___ ___ ___

H ___ ___ ___   U ___ ___ ___

I ___ ___ ___   V ___ ___ ___

J ___ ___ ___   W ___ ___ ___

K ___ ___ ___   X ___ ___ ___

L ___ ___ ___   Y ___ ___ ___

M ___ ___ ___   Z ___ ___ ___

Quality Cuisine Scavenger Hunt

In this game, you need to find foods that begin with the given letters. Three points for each item, with double points for items that begin with "q" or "x". The category for this round: ANYTHING ABOUT THINGS WE EAT.

A _____

B _____

C _____

D _____

E _____

F _____

G _____

H _____

I _____

J _____

K _____

L _____

M _____

N _____

O _____

P _____

Q _____

R _____

S _____

T _____

U _____

V _____

W _____

X _____

Y _____

Z _____

Scientific Scavenger Hunt

In this game, you need to find words that begin with the given letters. Ten points for each word, with double points for words that begin with "q" or "x". The category for this round: THINGS TO DO WITH SCIENCE.

A ___ ___ ___ ___

B ___ ___ ___ ___

C ___ ___ ___ ___

D ___ ___ ___ ___

E ___ ___ ___ ___

F ___ ___ ___ ___

G ___ ___ ___ ___

H ___ ___ ___ ___

I ___ ___ ___ ___

J ___ ___ ___ ___

K ___ ___ ___ ___

L ___ ___ ___ ___

M ___ ___ ___ ___

N ___ ___ ___ ___

O ___ ___ ___ ___

P ___ ___ ___ ___

Q ___ ___ ___ ___

R ___ ___ ___ ___

S ___ ___ ___ ___

T ___ ___ ___ ___

U ___ ___ ___ ___

V ___ ___ ___ ___

W ___ ___ ___ ___

X ___ ___ ___ ___

Y ___ ___ ___ ___

Z ___ ___ ___ ___

Sentimental Scavenger Hunt

In this game, you need to find words that begin with the given letters. Three points for each word, with double points for words that begin with "q" or "x". The category for this round: TYPES OF EMOTIONS (words that describe feelings).

A _____ _____ _____

B _____ _____ _____

C _____ _____ _____

D _____ _____ _____

E _____ _____ _____

F _____ _____ _____

G _____ _____ _____

H _____ _____ _____

I _____ _____ _____

J _____ _____ _____

K _____ _____ _____

L _____ _____ _____

M _____ _____ _____

N _____ _____ _____

O _____ _____ _____

P _____ _____ _____

Q _____ _____ _____

R _____ _____ _____

S _____ _____ _____

T _____ _____ _____

U _____ _____ _____

V _____ _____ _____

W _____ _____ _____

X _____ _____ _____

Y _____ _____ _____

Z _____ _____ _____

Stately Scavenger Hunt

In this game, you need to find words or phrases that begin with the given letters. Twenty points for each word or phrase, with double points for items that begin with "q" or "x". The category for this round: THINGS FOUND IN MY STATE.

A _____

B _____

C _____

D _____

E _____

F _____

G _____

H _____

I _____

J _____

K _____

L _____

M _____

N _____

O _____

P _____

Q _____

R _____

S _____

T _____

U _____

V _____

W _____

X _____

Y _____

Z _____

Summer School Scavenger Hunt

In this game, you need to find words that begin with the given letters. Ten points for each word, with double points for words that begin with "q" or "x", 25 points for phrases. The category for this round: THINGS YOU SEE ON THE PLAYGROUND.

A _____   N _____

B _____   O _____

C _____   P _____

D _____   Q _____

E _____   R _____

F _____   S _____

G _____   T _____

H _____   U _____

I _____   V _____

J _____   W _____

K _____   X _____

L _____   Y _____

M _____   Z _____

Things to Do Scavenger Hunt

In this game, you need to find words or phrases that begin with the given letters. Five points for each word or phrase, with double points for items that begin with "q" or "x". The category for this round: HOW TO HAVE A GREAT DAY OFF.

A _____   N _____

B _____   O _____

C _____   P _____

D _____   Q _____

E _____   R _____

F _____   S _____

G _____   T _____

H _____   U _____

I _____   V _____

J _____   W _____

K _____   X _____

L _____   Y _____

M _____   Z _____

Traveling Scavenger Hunt

In this game, you need to find words or phrases that begin with the given letters. Five points for each idea, with double points for items that begin with "q" or "x". The category for this round: PLACES TO GO FOR SCHOOL FIELD TRIPS.

A _____

B _____

C _____

D _____

E _____

F _____

G _____

H _____

I _____

J _____

K _____

L _____

M _____

N _____

O _____

P _____

Q _____

R _____

S _____

T _____

U _____

V _____

W _____

X _____

Y _____

Z _____

Vacation Scavenger Hunt

In this game, you need to find words or phrases that begin with the given letters. Ten points for each idea, with double points for items that begin with "q" or "x". The category for this round: Things you did during your vacation.

A _____   N _____

B _____   O _____

C _____   P _____

D _____   Q _____

E _____   R _____

F _____   S _____

G _____   T _____

H _____   U _____

I _____   V _____

J _____   W _____

K _____   X _____

L _____   Y _____

M _____   Z _____

Verb Scavenger Hunt

In this game, you need to find words or phrases that begin with the given letters. Three points for each word, with double points for words or phrases that begin with "q" or "x". The category this round: **Verbs: ACTION WORDS.**

A _____   N _____

B _____   O _____

C _____   P _____

D _____   Q _____

E _____   R _____

F _____   S _____

G _____   T _____

H _____   U _____

I _____   V _____

J _____   W _____

K _____   X _____

L _____   Y _____

M _____   Z _____

Your Own Scavenger Hunt

In this game, you need to find words or phrases that begin with the given letters. Ten points for each word or phrase, with double points for items that begin with "q" or "x". The category for this round: WORDS THAT DESCRIBE YOU!!!

A _____

B _____

C _____

D _____

E _____

F _____

G _____

H _____

I _____

J _____

K _____

L _____

M _____

N _____

O _____

P _____

Q _____

R _____

S _____

T _____

U _____

V _____

W _____

X _____

Y _____

Z _____

Word Chains

Word Chunking, Vocabulary Expansion

-ay (say, day)	**-ot** (pot, hot)	**-op** (mop, hop)	**-ob** (job, rob)
-ill (hill, fill)	**-ing** (wing, ring)	**-in** (pin, tin)	**-ock** (dock, clock)
-ip (ship, trip)	**-ap** (tap, gap)	**-an** (pan, can)	**-ale** (pale, tale)
-at (fat, cat)	**-unk** (junk, skunk)	**-est** (best, rest)	**-ine** (line, fine)
-am (jam, ham)	**-ail** (pail, hail)	**-ink** (pink, link)	**-ight** (right, light)
-ag (bag, lag)	**-ain** (rain, train)	**-ow** (bow, cow)	**-im** (him, swim)
-ack (sack, lack)	**-eed** (seed, reed)	**-ew** (few, new)	**-uck** (duck, luck)
-ank (tank, sank)	**-y** (my, cry)	**-ore** (core, more)	**-um** (gum, drum)
-ick (pick, quick)	**-out** (pout, tout)	**-ed** (red, bed)	
-ell (tell, fell)	**-ug** (bug, tug)	**-ab** (cab, jab)	

These puzzles are most appropriate for:

*
**
***

WORD CHAINS

To find words, go letter to letter either horizontally, vertically or diagonally. Don't use the same square twice in a single word, or jump a square to get to a letter you need.
Misspelled words don't count.

A	D	S	M
W	H	A	B
I	L	Y	R
D	L	T	R

Three Letter Words
(2 pts each)

___ ___

___ ___

___ ___

___ ___

___ ___

___ ___

___ ___

___ ___

___ ___

___ ___

Four Letter Words
(5 pts each)

____ ____

____ ____

____ ____

____ ____

____ ____

____ ____

Five Letter Words (8 pts each)

_____ _____

_____ _____

_____ _____

Six+ Letter Words
(10 pts each)

_____

_____

_____

_____

_____

_____

_____

_____

_____

_____

WORD CHAINS

To find words, go letter to letter either horizontally, vertically or diagonally. Don't use the same square twice in a single word, or jump a square to get to a letter you need. Misspelled words don't count.

B	L	D	O
L	A	C	U
J	G	T	B
S	U	R	E

Three Letter Words
(2 pts each)

_ _ _   _ _ _

_ _ _   _ _ _

_ _ _

_ _ _

_ _ _

_ _ _

_ _ _

_ _ _   _ _ _

_ _ _

_ _ _

Four Letter Words
(5 pts each)

_ _ _ _   _ _ _ _

_ _ _ _   _ _ _ _

_ _ _ _   _ _ _ _

_ _ _ _   _ _ _ _

_ _ _ _   _ _ _ _

_ _ _ _   _ _ _ _

Five Letter Words (8 pts each)

_ _ _ _ _   _ _ _ _ _

_ _ _ _ _   _ _ _ _ _

_ _ _ _ _   _ _ _ _ _

Six+ Letter Words
(10 pts each)

_ _ _ _ _ _

_ _ _ _ _ _

_ _ _ _ _ _

_ _ _ _ _ _

_ _ _ _ _ _

_ _ _ _ _ _

_ _ _ _ _ _

_ _ _ _ _ _

_ _ _ _ _ _

_ _ _ _ _ _

WORD CHAINS

To find words, go letter to letter either horizontally, vertically or diagonally. Don't use the same square twice in a single word, or jump a square to get to a letter you need. Misspelled words don't count.

C	K	T	A
U	O	R	P
D	L	C	E
F	I	L	B

Three Letter Words
(2 pts each)

___ ___

___ ___

___ ___

___ ___

___ ___

___ ___

___ ___

___ ___

___ ___

___ ___

Four Letter Words
(5 pts each)

____ ____

____ ____

____ ____

____ ____

Five Letter Words (8 pts each)

_____ _____

_____ _____

_____ _____

Six+ Letter Words
(10 pts each)

_____

_____

_____

_____

_____

_____

_____

_____

_____

WORD CHAINS

To find words, go letter to letter either horizontally, vertically or diagonally. Don't use the same square twice in a single word, or jump a square to get to a letter you need.
Misspelled words don't count.

C	T	M	E
R	A	F	A
P	D	S	J
L	I	H	T

Three Letter Words
(2 pts each)

_ _ _ _ _ _

_ _ _ _ _ _

_ _ _ _ _ _

_ _ _ _ _ _

_ _ _ _ _ _

_ _ _ _ _ _

_ _ _ _ _ _

_ _ _ _ _ _

_ _ _ _ _ _

_ _ _ _ _ _

Four Letter Words
(5 pts each)

_ _ _ _ _ _ _ _

_ _ _ _ _ _ _ _

_ _ _ _ _ _ _ _

_ _ _ _ _ _ _ _

_ _ _ _ _ _ _ _

_ _ _ _ _ _ _ _

Five Letter Words (8 pts each)

_ _ _ _ _ _ _ _ _ _

_ _ _ _ _ _ _ _ _ _

_ _ _ _ _ _ _ _ _ _

Six+ Letter Words
(10 pts each)

_ _ _ _ _ _

_ _ _ _ _ _

_ _ _ _ _ _

_ _ _ _ _ _

_ _ _ _ _ _

_ _ _ _ _ _

_ _ _ _ _ _

_ _ _ _ _ _

_ _ _ _ _ _

_ _ _ _ _ _

WORD CHAINS

To find words, go letter to letter either horizontally, vertically or diagonally. Don't use the same square twice in a single word, or jump a square to get to a letter you need. Misspelled words don't count.

E	A	K	E
H	S	N	R
L	E	T	A
Z	L	E	B

Three Letter Words
(2 pts each)

Four Letter Words
(5 pts each)

Six+ Letter Words
(10 pts each)

_ _ _   _ _ _   _ _ _ _   _ _ _ _   _ _ _ _ _ _   _ _ _ _ _ _

_ _ _   _ _ _   _ _ _ _   _ _ _ _   _ _ _ _ _ _   _ _ _ _ _ _

_ _ _   _ _ _   _ _ _ _   _ _ _ _   _ _ _ _ _ _   _ _ _ _ _ _

_ _ _   _ _ _   _ _ _ _   _ _ _ _   _ _ _ _ _ _   _ _ _ _ _ _

_ _ _   _ _ _   _ _ _ _   _ _ _ _   _ _ _ _ _ _   _ _ _ _ _ _

_ _ _   _ _ _   _ _ _ _   _ _ _ _   _ _ _ _ _ _   _ _ _ _ _ _

_ _ _   _ _ _   _ _ _ _   _ _ _ _   _ _ _ _ _ _   _ _ _ _ _ _

Five Letter Words (8 pts each)

_ _ _   _ _ _   _ _ _ _ _   _ _ _ _ _   _ _ _ _ _ _   _ _ _ _ _ _

_ _ _   _ _ _   _ _ _ _ _   _ _ _ _ _   _ _ _ _ _ _   _ _ _ _ _ _

_ _ _   _ _ _   _ _ _ _ _   _ _ _ _ _   _ _ _ _ _ _   _ _ _ _ _ _

_ _ _   _ _ _   _ _ _ _ _   _ _ _ _ _   _ _ _ _ _ _   _ _ _ _ _ _

WORD CHAINS

To find words, go letter to letter either horizontally, vertically or diagonally. Don't use the same square twice in a single word, or jump a square to get to a letter you need. Misspelled words don't count.

E	B	M	P
R	T	R	K
O	S	A	C
E	T	H	L

Three Letter Words
(2 pts each)

___ ___

___ ___

___ ___

___ ___

___ ___

___ ___

___ ___

___ ___

___ ___

___ ___

Four Letter Words
(5 pts each)

____ ____

____ ____

____ ____

____ ____

____ ____

____ ____

Five Letter Words (8 pts each)

_____ _____

_____ _____

Six+ Letter Words
(10 pts each)

_____

_____

_____

_____

_____

_____

_____

_____

_____

_____

WORD CHAINS

To find words, go letter to letter either horizontally, vertically or diagonally. Don't use the same square twice in a single word, or jump a square to get to a letter you need. Misspelled words don't count.

E	H	J	R
T	S	A	I
E	P	N	L
M	D	I	K

Three Letter Words
(2 pts each)

Four Letter Words
(5 pts each)

Six+ Letter Words
(10 pts each)

‒ ‒ ‒   ‒ ‒ ‒   ‒ ‒ ‒ ‒   ‒ ‒ ‒ ‒   ‒ ‒ ‒ ‒ ‒ ‒

‒ ‒ ‒   ‒ ‒ ‒   ‒ ‒ ‒ ‒   ‒ ‒ ‒ ‒   ‒ ‒ ‒ ‒ ‒ ‒

‒ ‒ ‒   ‒ ‒ ‒   ‒ ‒ ‒ ‒   ‒ ‒ ‒ ‒   ‒ ‒ ‒ ‒ ‒ ‒

‒ ‒ ‒   ‒ ‒ ‒   ‒ ‒ ‒ ‒   ‒ ‒ ‒ ‒   ‒ ‒ ‒ ‒ ‒ ‒

‒ ‒ ‒   ‒ ‒ ‒   ‒ ‒ ‒ ‒   ‒ ‒ ‒ ‒   ‒ ‒ ‒ ‒ ‒ ‒

‒ ‒ ‒   ‒ ‒ ‒   **Five Letter Words (8 pts each)**   ‒ ‒ ‒ ‒ ‒ ‒

‒ ‒ ‒   ‒ ‒ ‒   ‒ ‒ ‒ ‒ ‒   ‒ ‒ ‒ ‒ ‒   ‒ ‒ ‒ ‒ ‒ ‒

‒ ‒ ‒   ‒ ‒ ‒   ‒ ‒ ‒ ‒ ‒   ‒ ‒ ‒ ‒ ‒   ‒ ‒ ‒ ‒ ‒ ‒

‒ ‒ ‒   ‒ ‒ ‒   ‒ ‒ ‒ ‒ ‒   ‒ ‒ ‒ ‒ ‒   ‒ ‒ ‒ ‒ ‒ ‒

WORD CHAINS

To find words, go letter to letter either horizontally, vertically or diagonally. Don't use the same square twice in a single word, or jump a square to get to a letter you need. Misspelled words don't count.

E	K	M	H
R	N	T	O
W	I	P	N
L	F	E	R

Three Letter Words
(2 pts each)

___ ___   ___ ___

___ ___   ___ ___

___ ___   ___ ___

___ ___   ___ ___

___ ___   ___ ___

___ ___   ___ ___

___ ___   ___ ___

___ ___   ___ ___

___ ___   ___ ___

___ ___   ___ ___

Four Letter Words
(5 pts each)

___ ___   ___ ___

___ ___   ___ ___

___ ___   ___ ___

___ ___   ___ ___

___ ___   ___ ___

___ ___   ___ ___

Five Letter Words (8 pts each)

___ ___   ___ ___

___ ___   ___ ___

___ ___   ___ ___

Six+ Letter Words
(10 pts each)

___ ___   ___ ___

___ ___   ___ ___

___ ___   ___ ___

___ ___   ___ ___

___ ___   ___ ___

___ ___   ___ ___

___ ___   ___ ___

___ ___   ___ ___

___ ___   ___ ___

___ ___   ___ ___

WORD CHAINS

To find words, go letter to letter either horizontally, vertically or diagonally. Don't use the same square twice in a single word, or jump a square to get to a letter you need. Misspelled words don't count.

E	R	O	L
P	T	D	B
H	O	U	T
S	L	D	R

Three Letter Words
(2 pts each)

___ ___

___ ___

___ ___

___ ___

___ ___

___ ___

___ ___

___ ___

___ ___

___ ___

Four Letter Words
(5 pts each)

____ ____

____ ____

____ ____

____ ____

____ ____

____ ____

Five Letter Words (8 pts each)

_____ _____

_____ _____

Six+ Letter Words
(10 pts each)

_____

_____

_____

_____

_____

_____

_____

_____

_____

_____

WORD CHAINS

To find words, go letter to letter either horizontally, vertically or diagonally. Don't use the same square twice in a single word, or jump a square to get to a letter you need. Misspelled words don't count.

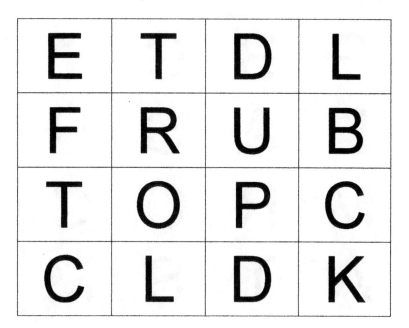

E	T	D	L
F	R	U	B
T	O	P	C
C	L	D	K

Three Letter Words
(2 pts each)

_ _ _   _ _ _

_ _ _   _ _ _

_ _ _   _ _ _

_ _ _   _ _ _

_ _ _   _ _ _

_ _ _   _ _ _

_ _ _   _ _ _

_ _ _   _ _ _

_ _ _   _ _ _

_ _ _   _ _ _

Four Letter Words
(5 pts each)

_ _ _ _   _ _ _ _

_ _ _ _   _ _ _ _

_ _ _ _   _ _ _ _

_ _ _ _   _ _ _ _

_ _ _ _   _ _ _ _

_ _ _ _   _ _ _ _

Five Letter Words (8 pts each)

_ _ _ _ _   _ _ _ _ _

_ _ _ _ _   _ _ _ _ _

Six+ Letter Words
(10 pts each)

_ _ _ _ _ _

_ _ _ _ _ _

_ _ _ _ _ _

_ _ _ _ _ _

_ _ _ _ _ _

_ _ _ _ _ _

_ _ _ _ _ _

_ _ _ _ _ _

_ _ _ _ _ _

_ _ _ _ _ _

WORD CHAINS

To find words, go letter to letter either horizontally, vertically or diagonally. Don't use the same square twice in a single word, or jump a square to get to a letter you need. Misspelled words don't count.

G	B	C	T
E	A	S	H
M	R	O	C
A	T	S	M

Three Letter Words
(2 pts each)

___ ___   ___ ___

___ ___   ___ ___

___ ___   ___ ___

___ ___   ___ ___

___ ___   ___ ___

___ ___   ___ ___

___ ___   ___ ___

___ ___   ___ ___

___ ___   ___ ___

___ ___   ___ ___

Four Letter Words
(5 pts each)

____ ____   ____ ____

____ ____   ____ ____

____ ____   ____ ____

____ ____   ____ ____

____ ____   ____ ____

____ ____   ____ ____

Five Letter Words (8 pts each)

_____ _____

_____ _____

_____ _____

_____ _____

Six+ Letter Words
(10 pts each)

_____

_____

_____

_____

_____

_____

_____

_____

_____

_____

WORD CHAINS

To find words, go letter to letter either horizontally, vertically or diagonally. Don't use the same square twice in a single word, or jump a square to get to a letter you need. Misspelled words don't count.

H	S	G	K
T	A	N	Y
O	K	I	R
C	W	B	L

Three Letter Words
(2 pts each)

___ ___

___ ___

___ ___

___ ___

___ ___

___ ___

___ ___

___ ___

___ ___

___ ___

___ ___

Four Letter Words
(5 pts each)

____ ____

____ ____

____ ____

____ ____

____ ____

____ ____

Five Letter Words (8 pts each)

_____ _____

_____ _____

_____ _____

_____ _____

Six+ Letter Words
(10 pts each)

_____

_____

_____

_____

_____

_____

_____

_____

_____

_____

WORD CHAINS

To find words, go letter to letter either horizontally, vertically or diagonally. Don't use the same square twice in a single word, or jump a square to get to a letter you need. Misspelled words don't count.

H	T	U	G
W	I	R	B
D	E	O	J
E	F	L	S

Three Letter Words
(2 pts each)

___ ___

___ ___

___ ___

___ ___

___ ___

___ ___

___ ___

___ ___

___ ___

___ ___

Four Letter Words
(5 pts each)

____ ____

____ ____

____ ____

____ ____

____ ____

____ ____

Five Letter Words (8 pts each)

_____ _____

_____ _____

Six+ Letter Words
(10 pts each)

_____

_____

_____

_____

_____

_____

_____

_____

_____

_____

WORD CHAINS

To find words, go letter to letter either horizontally, vertically or diagonally. Don't use the same square twice in a single word, or jump a square to get to a letter you need. Misspelled words don't count.

H	W	E	K
D	A	T	N
Y	P	I	L
O	W	H	E

Three Letter Words
(2 pts each)

___ ___   ___ ___

___ ___   ___ ___

___ ___   ___ ___

___ ___   ___ ___

___ ___   ___ ___

___ ___   ___ ___

___ ___   ___ ___

___ ___   ___ ___

___ ___   ___ ___

___ ___   ___ ___

Four Letter Words
(5 pts each)

___ ___ ___ ___   ___ ___ ___ ___

___ ___ ___ ___   ___ ___ ___ ___

___ ___ ___ ___   ___ ___ ___ ___

___ ___ ___ ___   ___ ___ ___ ___

___ ___ ___ ___   ___ ___ ___ ___

___ ___ ___ ___   ___ ___ ___ ___

Five Letter Words (8 pts each)

___ ___ ___ ___ ___   ___ ___ ___ ___ ___

___ ___ ___ ___ ___   ___ ___ ___ ___ ___

Six+ Letter Words
(10 pts each)

___ ___ ___ ___ ___ ___

___ ___ ___ ___ ___ ___

___ ___ ___ ___ ___ ___

___ ___ ___ ___ ___ ___

___ ___ ___ ___ ___ ___

___ ___ ___ ___ ___ ___

___ ___ ___ ___ ___ ___

___ ___ ___ ___ ___ ___

___ ___ ___ ___ ___ ___

___ ___ ___ ___ ___ ___

WORD CHAINS

To find words, go letter to letter either horizontally, vertically or diagonally. Don't use the same square twice in a single word, or jump a square to get to a letter you need. Misspelled words don't count.

I	H	P	F
T	J	A	C
E	M	R	T
N	F	I	B

Three Letter Words
(2 pts each)

___   ___

___   ___

___   ___

___   ___

___   ___

___   ___

___   ____

___   ___

___   ___

Four Letter Words
(5 pts each)

____   ____

____   ____

____   ____

____   ____

Five Letter Words (8 pts each)

_____   _____

_____   _____

Six+ Letter Words
(10 pts each)

_____

_____

_____

_____

_____

_____

_____

_____

_____

_____

WORD CHAINS

To find words, go letter to letter either horizontally, vertically or diagonally. Don't use the same square twice in a single word, or jump a square to get to a letter you need. Misspelled words don't count.

I	T	O	L
M	S	B	P
Q	U	E	N
A	R	J	F

Three Letter Words
(2 pts each)

___ ___

___ ___

___ ___

___ ___

___ ___

___ ___

___ ___

___ ___

___ ___

___ ___

___ ___

Four Letter Words
(5 pts each)

____ ____

____ ____

____ ____

____ ____

____ ____

____ ____

____ ____

Five Letter Words (8 pts each)

_____ _____

_____ _____

_____ _____

Six+ Letter Words
(10 pts each)

_____

_____

_____

_____

_____

_____

_____

_____

_____

_____

WORD CHAINS

To find words, go letter to letter either horizontally, vertically or diagonally. Don't use the same square twice in a single word, or jump a square to get to a letter you need. Misspelled words don't count.

J	A	D	H
K	C	S	E
Q	I	T	A
U	R	P	E

Three Letter Words
(2 pts each)

___ ___ ___ ___

___ ___ ___ ___

___ ___ ___ ___

___ ___ ___ ___

___ ___ ___ ___

___ ___ ___ ___

___ ___ ___ ___

Four Letter Words
(5 pts each)

___ ___ ___ ___ ___ ___ ___ ___

___ ___ ___ ___ ___ ___ ___ ___

___ ___ ___ ___ ___ ___ ___ ___

___ ___ ___ ___ ___ ___ ___ ___

___ ___ ___ ___ ___ ___ ___ ___

Five Letter Words (8 pts each)

___ ___ ___ ___ ___ ___ ___ ___ ___ ___

___ ___ ___ ___ ___ ___ ___ ___ ___ ___

___ ___ ___ ___ ___ ___ ___ ___ ___ ___

Six+ Letter Words
(10 pts each)

___ ___ ___ ___ ___ ___

___ ___ ___ ___ ___ ___

___ ___ ___ ___ ___ ___

___ ___ ___ ___ ___ ___

___ ___ ___ ___ ___ ___

___ ___ ___ ___ ___ ___

___ ___ ___ ___ ___ ___

___ ___ ___ ___ ___ ___

___ ___ ___ ___ ___ ___

___ ___ ___ ___ ___ ___

WORD CHAINS

To find words, go letter to letter either horizontally, vertically or diagonally. Don't use the same square twice in a single word, or jump a square to get to a letter you need. Misspelled words don't count.

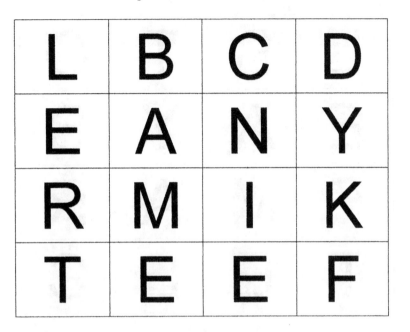

Three Letter Words (2 pts each)	Four Letter Words (5 pts each)	Six+ Letter Words (10 pts each)

Three Letter Words
(2 pts each)

Four Letter Words
(5 pts each)

Six+ Letter Words
(10 pts each)

___ ___   ___ ___   ____ ____   ____ ____   _____ _____

___ ___   ___ ___   ____ ____   ____ ____   _____ _____

___ ___   ___ ___   ____ ____   ____ ____   _____ _____

___ ___   ___ ___   ____ ____   ____ ____   _____ _____

___ ___   ___ ___   ____ ____   ____ ____   _____ _____

___ ___   ___ ___   ____ ____   ____ ____   _____ _____

___ ___   ___ ___   Five Letter Words (8 pts each)   _____ _____

___ ___   ___ ___   _____ _____   _____ _____   _____ _____

___ ___   ___ ___   _____ _____   _____ _____   _____ _____

___ ___   ___ ___   _____ _____   _____ _____   _____ _____

___ ___   ___ ___   WORD —— _____ _____   _____ _____

WORD CHAINS

To find words, go letter to letter either horizontally, vertically or diagonally. Don't use the same square twice in a single word, or jump a square to get to a letter you need. Misspelled words don't count.

L	B	T	O
E	A	Y	B
F	M	A	R
T	E	E	C

Three Letter Words
(2 pts each)

___ ___

___ ___

___ ___

___ ___

___ ___

___ ___

___ ___

___ ___

___ ___

___ ___

Four Letter Words
(5 pts each)

____ ____

____ ____

____ ____

____ ____

____ ____

Five Letter Words (8 pts each)

_____ _____

_____ _____

_____ _____

Six+ Letter Words
(10 pts each)

_____

_____

_____

_____

_____

_____

_____

_____

_____

_____

WORD CHAINS

To find words, go letter to letter either horizontally, vertically or diagonally. Don't use the same square twice in a single word, or jump a square to get to a letter you need. Misspelled words don't count.

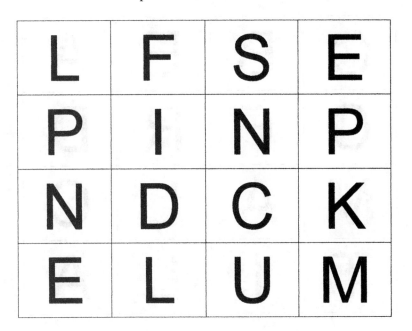

Three Letter Words
(2 pts each)

_ _ _   _ _ _

_ _ _   _ _ _

_ _ _   _ _ _

_ _ _   _ _ _

_ _ _   _ _ _

_ _ _   _ _ _

_ _ _   _ _ _

_ _ _   _ _ _

_ _ _   _ _ _

_ _ _   _ _ _

Four Letter Words
(5 pts each)

_ _ _ _   _ _ _ _

_ _ _ _   _ _ _ _

_ _ _ _   _ _ _ _

_ _ _ _   _ _ _ _

_ _ _ _   _ _ _ _

_ _ _ _   _ _ _ _

Five Letter Words (8 pts each)

_ _ _ _ _   _ _ _ _ _

_ _ _ _ _   _ _ _ _ _

_ _ _ _ _   _ _ _ _ _

Six+ Letter Words
(10 pts each)

_ _ _ _ _ _

_ _ _ _ _ _

_ _ _ _ _ _

_ _ _ _ _ _

_ _ _ _ _ _

_ _ _ _ _ _

_ _ _ _ _ _

_ _ _ _ _ _

_ _ _ _ _ _

_ _ _ _ _ _

WORD CHAINS

To find words, go letter to letter either horizontally, vertically or diagonally. Don't use the same square twice in a single word, or jump a square to get to a letter you need. Misspelled words don't count.

O	B	E	A
C	F	R	D
M	A	L	C
T	I	L	A

Three Letter Words
(2 pts each)

___ ___   ___ ___

___ ___   ___ ___

___ ___   ___ ___

___ ___   ___ ___

___ ___   ___ ___

___ ___   ___ ___

___ ___   ___ ___

___ ___   ___ ___

___ ___   ___ ___

___ ___   ___ ___

Four Letter Words
(5 pts each)

___ ___   ___ ___

___ ___   ___ ___

___ ___   ___ ___

___ ___   ___ ___

___ ___   ___ ___

Five Letter Words (8 pts each)

___ ___ ___   ___ ___ ___

___ ___ ___   ___ ___ ___

___ ___ ___   ___ ___ ___

Six+ Letter Words
(10 pts each)

___ ___ ___

___ ___ ___

___ ___ ___

___ ___ ___

___ ___ ___

___ ___ ___

___ ___ ___

___ ___ ___

___ ___ ___

WORD CHAINS

To find words, go letter to letter either horizontally, vertically or diagonally. Don't use the same square twice in a single word, or jump a square to get to a letter you need. Misspelled words don't count.

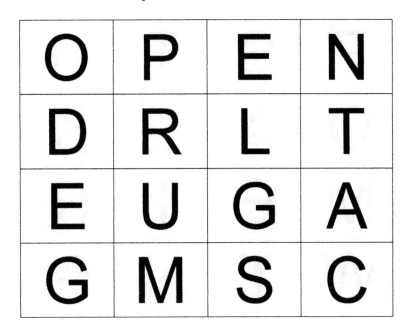

Three Letter Words	Four Letter Words	Six+ Letter Words
(2 pts each)	(5 pts each)	(10 pts each)

Three Letter Words
(2 pts each)

Four Letter Words
(5 pts each)

Six+ Letter Words
(10 pts each)

___ ___   ____ ____   _____

___ ___   ____ ____   _____

___ ___   ____ ____   _____

___ ___   ____ ____   _____

___ ___   ____ ____   _____

___ ___   ____ ____   _____

___ ___   ____ ____   _____

Five Letter Words (8 pts each)

___ ___   _____ _____   _____

___ ___   _____ _____   _____

___ ___   _____ _____   _____

WORD CHAINS

To find words, go letter to letter either horizontally, vertically or diagonally. Don't use the same square twice in a single word, or jump a square to get to a letter you need. Misspelled words don't count.

P	S	T	U
O	A	L	K
M	E	I	R
W	T	N	G

Three Letter Words
(2 pts each)

___ ___ ___ ___

___ ___ ___ ___

___ ___ ___ ___

___ ___ ___ ___

___ ___ ___ ___

___ ___ ___ ___

___ ___ ___ ___

___ ___ ___ ___

___ ___ ___ ___

___ ___ ___ ___

Four Letter Words
(5 pts each)

____ ____ ____ ____

____ ____ ____ ____

____ ____ ____ ____

____ ____ ____ ____

____ ____ ____ ____

____ ____ ____ ____

Five Letter Words (8 pts each)

_____ _____ _____

_____ _____ _____

_____ _____ _____

Six+ Letter Words
(10 pts each)

_____

_____

_____

_____

_____

_____

_____

_____

_____

_____

WORD CHAINS

To find words, go letter to letter either horizontally, vertically or diagonally. Don't use the same square twice in a single word, or jump a square to get to a letter you need. Misspelled words don't count.

Q	A	T	R
W	P	I	F
A	I	S	L
D	R	H	E

Three Letter Words
(2 pts each)

___ ___

___ ___

___ ___

___ ___

___ ___

___ ___

___ ___

___ ___

___ ___

___ ___

___ ___

Four Letter Words
(5 pts each)

____ ____

____ ____

____ ____

____ ____

____ ____

____ ____

Five Letter Words (8 pts each)

_____ _____

_____ _____

_____ _____

Six+ Letter Words
(10 pts each)

_____

_____

_____

_____

_____

_____

_____

_____

_____

WORD CHAINS

To find words, go letter to letter either horizontally, vertically or diagonally. Don't use the same square twice in a single word, or jump a square to get to a letter you need. Misspelled words don't count.

R	B	C	R
F	A	T	E
M	I	S	M
H	W	A	N

Three Letter Words
(2 pts each)

— — — — — —

— — — — — —

— — — — — —

— — — — — —

— — — — — —

— — — — — —

— — — — — —

— — — — — —

— — — — — —

— — — — — —

Four Letter Words
(5 pts each)

— — — — — — — —

— — — — — — — —

— — — — — — — —

— — — — — — — —

— — — — — — — —

— — — — — — — —

Five Letter Words (8 pts each)

— — — — — — — — — —

— — — — — — — — — —

— — — — — — — — — —

— — — — — — — — — —

Six+ Letter Words
(10 pts each)

— — — — — —

— — — — — —

— — — — — —

— — — — — —

— — — — — —

— — — — — —

— — — — — —

— — — — — —

— — — — — —

— — — — — —

WORD CHAINS

To find words, go letter to letter either horizontally, vertically or diagonally. Don't use the same square twice in a single word, or jump a square to get to a letter you need. Misspelled words don't count.

R	U	G	S
D	M	W	M
S	E	I	T
D	L	R	H

Three Letter Words
(2 pts each)

___ ___ ___   ___ ___ ___

___ ___ ___   ___ ___ ___

___ ___ ___   ___ ___ ___

___ ___ ___   ___ ___ ___

___ ___ ___   ___ ___ ___

___ ___ ___   ___ ___ ___

___ ___ ___   ___ ___ ___

___ ___ ___   ___ ___ ___

___ ___ ___   ___ ___ ___

___ ___ ___   ___ ___ ___

Four Letter Words
(5 pts each)

___ ___ ___ ___   ___ ___ ___ ___

___ ___ ___ ___   ___ ___ ___ ___

___ ___ ___ ___   ___ ___ ___ ___

___ ___ ___ ___   ___ ___ ___ ___

___ ___ ___ ___   ___ ___ ___ ___

___ ___ ___ ___   ___ ___ ___ ___

Five Letter Words ($1 each)

___ ___ ___ ___ ___   ___ ___ ___ ___ ___

___ ___ ___ ___ ___   ___ ___ ___ ___ ___

___ ___ ___ ___ ___   ___ ___ ___ ___ ___

Six+ Letter Words
(10 pts each)

___ ___ ___ ___ ___ ___

___ ___ ___ ___ ___ ___

___ ___ ___ ___ ___ ___

___ ___ ___ ___ ___ ___

___ ___ ___ ___ ___ ___

___ ___ ___ ___ ___ ___

___ ___ ___ ___ ___ ___

___ ___ ___ ___ ___ ___

___ ___ ___ ___ ___ ___

___ ___ ___ ___ ___ ___

WORD CHAINS

To find words, go letter to letter either horizontally, vertically or diagonally. Don't use the same square twice in a single word, or jump a square to get to a letter you need. Misspelled words don't count.

R	I	L	A
G	M	T	R
H	E	A	K
J	T	C	B

Three Letter Words
(2 pts each)

___ ___ ___   ___ ___ ___

___ ___ ___   ___ ___ ___

___ ___ ___   ___ ___ ___

___ ___ ___   ___ ___ ___

___ ___ ___   ___ ___ ___

___ ___ ___   ___ ___ ___

___ ___ ___   ___ ___ ___

Four Letter Words
(5 pts each)

___ ___ ___ ___   ___ ___ ___ ___

___ ___ ___ ___   ___ ___ ___ ___

___ ___ ___ ___   ___ ___ ___ ___

___ ___ ___ ___   ___ ___ ___ ___

___ ___ ___ ___   ___ ___ ___ ___

___ ___ ___ ___   ___ ___ ___ ___

Five Letter Words (8 pts each)

___ ___ ___ ___ ___   ___ ___ ___ ___ ___

___ ___ ___ ___ ___   ___ ___ ___ ___ ___

___ ___ ___ ___ ___   ___ ___ ___ ___ ___

Six+ Letter Words
(10 pts each)

___ ___ ___ ___ ___ ___

___ ___ ___ ___ ___ ___

___ ___ ___ ___ ___ ___

___ ___ ___ ___ ___ ___

___ ___ ___ ___ ___ ___

___ ___ ___ ___ ___ ___

___ ___ ___ ___ ___ ___

___ ___ ___ ___ ___ ___

___ ___ ___ ___ ___ ___

WORD CHAINS

To find words, go letter to letter either horizontally, vertically or diagonally. Don't use the same square twice in a single word, or jump a square to get to a letter you need. Misspelled words don't count.

R	O	P	B
T	S	A	C
J	F	K	T
P	U	N	K

Three Letter Words
(2 pts each)

--- ---

--- ---

--- ---

--- ---

--- ---

--- ---

--- ---

--- ---

--- ---

--- ---

Four Letter Words
(5 pts each)

---- ----

---- ----

---- ----

---- ----

---- ----

---- ----

Five Letter Words (8 pts each)

----- -----

----- -----

----- -----

Six+ Letter Words
(10 pts each)

------ ------

------ ------

------ ------

------ ------

------ ------

------ ------

------ ------

------ ------

------ ------

------ ------

WORD CHAINS

To find words, go letter to letter either horizontally, vertically or diagonally. Don't use
the same square twice in a single word, or jump a square to get to a letter you need.
Misspelled words don't count.

S	E	L	F
M	T	G	C
E	I	A	S
D	L	R	B

Three Letter Words
(2 pts each)

___ ___   ___ ___

___ ___   ___ ___

___ ___   ___ ___

___ ___   ___ ___

___ ___   ___ ___

___ ___   ___ ___

___ ___   ___ ___

Four Letter Words
(5 pts each)

___ ___ ___   ___ ___ ___

___ ___ ___   ___ ___ ___

___ ___ ___   ___ ___ ___

___ ___ ___   ___ ___ ___

Six+ Letter Words
(10 pts each)

___ ___ ___ ___ ___

___ ___ ___ ___ ___

___ ___ ___ ___ ___

___ ___ ___ ___ ___

Five Letter Words (8 pts each)

___ ___ ___ ___   ___ ___ ___ ___

___ ___ ___ ___   ___ ___ ___ ___

___ ___ ___ ___   ___ ___ ___ ___

___ ___ ___   ___ ___ ___

WORD CHAINS

To find words, go letter to letter either horizontally, vertically or diagonally. Don't use the same square twice in a single word, or jump a square to get to a letter you need. Misspelled words don't count.

S	J	L	R
K	T	O	C
E	I	A	B
D	N	R	F

Three Letter Words
(2 pts each)

_ _ _   _ _ _

_ _ _   _ _ _

_ _ _   _ _ _

_ _ _   _ _ _

_ _ _   _ _ _

_ _ _   _ _ _

_ _ _   _ _ _

_ _ _   _ _ _

_ _ _   _ _ _

_ _ _   _ _ _

Four Letter Words
(5 pts each)

_ _ _ _   _ _ _ _

_ _ _ _   _ _ _ _

_ _ _ _   _ _ _ _

_ _ _ _   _ _ _ _

_ _ _ _   _ _ _ _

_ _ _ _   _ _ _ _

Five Letter Words (8 pts each)

_ _ _ _ _   _ _ _ _ _

_ _ _ _ _   _ _ _ _ _

_ _ _ _ _   _ _ _ _ _

Six+ Letter Words
(10 pts each)

_ _ _ _ _ _

_ _ _ _ _ _

_ _ _ _ _ _

_ _ _ _ _ _

_ _ _ _ _ _

_ _ _ _ _ _

_ _ _ _ _ _

_ _ _ _ _ _

_ _ _ _ _ _

_ _ _ _ _ _

WORD CHAINS

To find words, go letter to letter either horizontally, vertically or diagonally. Don't use the same square twice in a single word, or jump a square to get to a letter you need. Misspelled words don't count.

S	P	W	H
E	L	I	F
A	L	M	S
T	K	F	E

Three Letter Words
(2 pts each)

_ _ _   _ _ _

_ _ _   _ _ _

_ _ _   _ _ _

_ _ _   _ _ _

_ _ _   _ _ _

_ _ _   _ _ _

_ _ _   _ _ _

_ _ _   _ _ _

_ _ _   _ _ _

_ _ _   _ _ _

Four Letter Words
(5 pts each)

_ _ _ _   _ _ _ _

_ _ _ _   _ _ _ _

_ _ _ _   _ _ _ _

_ _ _ _   _ _ _ _

_ _ _ _   _ _ _ _

_ _ _ _   _ _ _ _

Five Letter Words (8 pts each)

_ _ _ _ _   _ _ _ _ _

_ _ _ _ _   _ _ _ _ _

_ _ _ _ _   _ _ _ _ _

_ _ _ _ _   _ _ _ _ _

Six+ Letter Words
(10 pts each)

_ _ _ _ _ _

_ _ _ _ _ _

_ _ _ _ _ _

_ _ _ _ _ _

_ _ _ _ _ _

_ _ _ _ _ _

_ _ _ _ _ _

_ _ _ _ _ _

_ _ _ _ _ _

_ _ _ _ _ _

WORD CHAINS

To find words, go letter to letter either horizontally, vertically or diagonally. Don't use the same square twice in a single word, or jump a square to get to a letter you need. Misspelled words don't count.

S	T	H	M
N	E	W	I
F	E	R	O
M	D	T	A

Three Letter Words
(2 pts each)

___ ___

___ ___

___ ___

___ ___

___ ___

___ ___

___ ___

___ ___

___ ___

___ ___

___ ___

Four Letter Words
(5 pts each)

____ ____

____ ____

____ ____

____ ____

____ ____

____ ____

Five Letter Words (8 pts each)

_____ _____

_____ _____

_____ _____

Six+ Letter Words
(10 pts each)

_____

_____

_____

_____

_____

_____

_____

_____

_____

_____

WORD CHAINS

To find words, go letter to letter either horizontally, vertically or diagonally. Don't use the same square twice in a single word, or jump a square to get to a letter you need. Misspelled words don't count.

T	A	M	E
R	P	T	F
A	O	L	I
T	H	G	L

Three Letter Words
(2 pts each)

___ ___

___ ___

___ ___

___ ___

___ ___

___ ___

___ ___

___ ___

___ ___

___ ___

Four Letter Words
(5 pts each)

____ ____

____ ____

____ ____

____ ____

____ ____

Five Letter Words (8 pts each)

_____ _____

_____ _____

_____ _____

Six+ Letter Words
(10 pts each)

_____

_____

_____

_____

_____

_____

_____

_____

_____

_____

WORD CHAINS

To find words, go letter to letter either horizontally, vertically or diagonally. Don't use the same square twice in a single word, or jump a square to get to a letter you need. Misspelled words don't count.

T	E	F	A
G	R	O	R
E	A	M	C
T	L	P	E

Three Letter Words
(2 pts each)

___ ___   ___ ___

___ ___   ___ ___

___ ___   ___ ___

___ ___   ___ ___

___ ___   ___ ___

___ ___   ___ ___

___ ___   ___ ___

___ ___   ___ ___

___ ___   ___ ___

___ ___   ___ ___

Four Letter Words
(5 pts each)

___ ___ ___ ___   ___ ___ ___ ___

___ ___ ___ ___   ___ ___ ___ ___

___ ___ ___ ___   ___ ___ ___ ___

___ ___ ___ ___   ___ ___ ___ ___

___ ___ ___ ___   ___ ___ ___ ___

___ ___ ___ ___   ___ ___ ___ ___

Five Letter Words (8 pts each)

___ ___ ___ ___ ___   ___ ___ ___ ___ ___

___ ___ ___ ___ ___   ___ ___ ___ ___ ___

___ ___ ___ ___ ___   ___ ___ ___ ___ ___

Six+ Letter Words
(10 pts each)

___ ___ ___ ___ ___ ___

___ ___ ___ ___ ___ ___

___ ___ ___ ___ ___ ___

___ ___ ___ ___ ___ ___

___ ___ ___ ___ ___ ___

___ ___ ___ ___ ___ ___

___ ___ ___ ___ ___ ___

___ ___ ___ ___ ___ ___

___ ___ ___ ___ ___ ___

___ ___ ___ ___ ___ ___

WORD CHAINS

To find words, go letter to letter either horizontally, vertically or diagonally. Don't use the same square twice in a single word, or jump a square to get to a letter you need. Misspelled words don't count.

U	B	S	L
T	C	O	W
N	R	T	N
A	I	U	E

Three Letter Words
(2 pts each)

___ ___

___ ___

___ ___

___ ___

___ ___

___ ___

___ ___

___ ___

___ ___

___ ___

Four Letter Words
(5 pts each)

____ ____

____ ____

____ ____

____ ____

____ ____

____

Five Letter Words (8 pts each)

_____ _____

_____ _____

_____ _____

Six+ Letter Words
(10 pts each)

_____ _____

_____ _____

_____ _____

_____ _____

_____ _____

_____ _____

_____ _____

_____ _____

_____ _____

WORD CHAINS

To find words, go letter to letter either horizontally, vertically or diagonally. Don't use the same square twice in a single word, or jump a square to get to a letter you need. Misspelled words don't count.

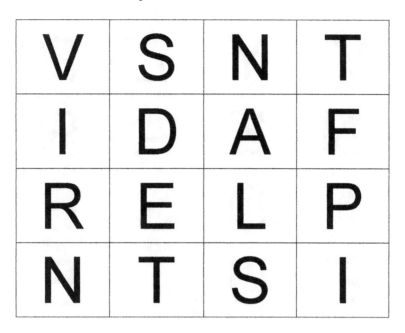

Three Letter Words (2 pts each)	Four Letter Words (5 pts each)	Six+ Letter Words (10 pts each)
___ ___	____ ____	_____
___ ___	____ ____	_____
___ ___	____ ____	_____
___ ___	____ ____	_____
___ ___	____ ____	_____
___ ___	____ ____	_____
___ ___	____ ____	_____

Five Letter Words (8 pts each)

___ ___	_____ _____	_____
___ ___	_____ _____	_____
___ ___	_____ _____	_____
___ ___	_____ _____	_____

WORD CHAINS

To find words, go letter to letter either horizontally, vertically or diagonally. Don't use
the same square twice in a single word, or jump a square to get to a letter you need.
Misspelled words don't count.

W	Y	L	P
N	E	A	R
F	D	S	B
R	U	T	E

Three Letter Words
(2 pts each)

___ ___

___ ___

___ ___

___ ___

___ ___

___ ___

___ ___

___ ___

___ ___

___ ___

___ ___

Four Letter Words
(5 pts each)

____ ____

____ ____

____ ____

____ ____

____ ____

____ ____

Five Letter Words (8 pts each)

_____ _____

_____ _____

_____ _____

_____ _____

Six+ Letter Words
(10 pts each)

_____

_____

_____

_____

_____

_____

_____

_____

_____

_____

WORD CHAINS

To find words, go letter to letter either horizontally, vertically or diagonally. Don't use the same square twice in a single word, or jump a square to get to a letter you need. Misspelled words don't count.

Y	T	R	I
E	B	L	P
L	F	I	H
A	L	S	W

Three Letter Words
(2 pts each)

___ ___

___ ___

___ ___

___ ___

___ ___

___ ___

___ ___

___ ___

___ ___

___ ___

Four Letter Words
(5 pts each)

____ ____

____ ____

____ ____

____ ____

____ ____

____ ____

Five Letter Words (8 pts each)

_____ _____

_____ _____

_____ _____

Six+ Letter Words
(10 pts each)

_____

_____

_____

_____

_____

_____

_____

_____

_____

_____

Word Searches

Vocabulary, Word Chunking, Finding Alternatives for "Tired Words"

These puzzles are most appropriate for:

*
**
***

Word Search Time

Find 50 words about autumn.

```
Y P B F S L C D S V J O S C I J K A H M R A W
C L U R L C D O H Q E A R T V R A X G V E E S
I F Z M E U A N R U U T C A O V Z G R V K L C
D I T Z P E R R A N A I E K N R K J I H W Z S
E E S B I K Z R E G S S R R E G M T F A N O W
R L S O B R I E Y C N T T R A T E Y U C C K T
P D V O R V D N Y Y R I A R E N D Z S C N K Y
L K A T O H Z L S R T O R L O L P A E I G H M
W C T S W U I H L M E I W E K N H R L Z C U Y
V V Q E N Z T U I A I T V Z H E O B E N E N Y
T B M C H I C S L U F R S I Z T O M U W L B O
L E X X O T G K M C X N G U T G A R Y F R E D
C O A T O X S Y F G M B I L L C C G Y I T Q H
U O T U D F L U P W R P S A I B A Y L S N E O
N E S W I N D G G X Q U J C R P R L R T L L D
F N O Q W I H M O V H E H H E R I U H B L A P
P L H K A E C R U A Q I A L E A B G A L Z O G
Y S G O S Z T U P S L R K B N D I T A Z R N A
E N E Y Q I I J E L V N N T U L E B L D I U U
K R L N N A W V Y E I A Z O N G E I N P T S D
R O P N A M A G S R R K L O E S N I A U Z D Q
U C P U D E D T P C Y C O V A G A E M U G M E
T A A S L N W S H B J M U B F R R N I T P Z Z
```

ACORN	BROWN	FIELD	MAIZE	SPRINKLE
ACTIVITY	CHILLY	FLURRY	MOONLIGHT	SQUIRREL
APPLE	CIDER	GATHERING	ORANGE	STORMY
ASTRONOMY	CLOUDBURST	GHOST	PILGRIMS	SUNNY
AUTUMN	COAT	GOBLIN	PUMPKIN	TURKEY
BASEBALL	CORNSTALK	HARVEST	RAINDROP	VEGETABLE
BLUSTERY	CRANBERRY	HOOD	RAINFALL	VETERAN
BOOTS	CRUNCHY	HUSK	REAPING	WARM
BREEZE	DAZZLING	JACKET	SCARECROW	WIND
BRILLIANT	DRIZZLY	LEAVES	SOCCER	WITCH

Word Search Time

OTHER WAYS TO SAY "BIG", "NICE", "GOOD" and "GOT"

```
S  H  F  H  U  O  W  Q  A  L  S  C  G  M  I  E  C  H  A  Q  V  K  K  J  P
U  U  M  R  S  A  B  M  C  V  O  Q  B  N  A  N  N  I  T  S  P  B  M  H  N
P  G  A  W  Z  L  G  O  C  O  M  D  H  A  I  G  C  J  T  O  Z  K  B  R  W
E  E  N  I  A  Q  E  Z  V  F  W  R  C  A  U  N  N  R  O  S  M  T  D  N  L
R  H  V  C  Y  U  W  V  Y  T  R  C  S  G  C  E  I  I  E  Y  A  E  Y  Z  H
B  E  H  P  E  C  M  W  J  A  O  T  S  O  X  E  L  A  F  D  A  T  H  H  K
Q  E  O  J  G  H  E  V  X  M  O  Q  U  C  G  A  N  U  T  I  I  B  N  E  N
G  R  T  D  C  X  L  Y  P  N  A  R  E  T  C  I  F  O  F  R  C  B  L  A  B
R  O  C  F  Q  N  R  L  I  G  T  L  C  Q  J  G  G  R  R  E  E  L  E  F
R  W  E  Y  D  R  I  S  N  E  L  E  U  K  A  P  O  A  I  M  E  T  N  E  W
I  C  M  Q  M  S  H  I  O  E  N  I  O  T  L  S  R  B  N  E  O  D  N  T  W
N  J  B  E  H  I  D  U  N  D  R  Z  H  E  J  D  P  E  T  T  N  U  N  E  C
R  O  F  E  N  N  S  T  D  E  X  E  A  R  J  G  Y  L  C  A  I  D  S  O  Q
T  L  D  G  U  D  Q  E  D  B  R  S  Q  V  O  M  C  T  E  E  I  C  L  W  W
J  G  L  O  L  H  V  C  P  E  A  A  L  W  C  L  V  U  K  N  I  N  W  Y  A
G  N  T  Z  P  E  O  G  D  N  L  I  K  R  R  I  W  S  F  E  D  V  E  Z  W
X  S  B  D  I  L  N  G  T  K  D  C  T  Y  N  I  K  E  A  M  Z  I  E  D  H
A  R  G  R  O  I  L  S  N  R  E  H  B  G  C  B  W  U  Q  N  T  H  D  D  B
H  U  T  S  T  O  P  J  O  Y  O  U  S  W  W  T  F  X  V  I  I  A  Q  E  C
S  E  S  I  R  A  Z  S  Q  H  K  J  E  Z  Z  A  Y  M  O  D  E  N  I  A  G
R  A  C  I  C  H  E  L  P  F  U  L  W  Y  X  M  D  X  A  V  D  A  B  T  I
L  X  O  I  P  L  W  C  F  T  H  B  N  R  T  E  W  U  E  V  I  T  S  E  F
E  U  O  K  I  N  D  C  G  B  Q  O  I  G  B  Z  P  C  L  A  I  D  R  O  C
S  U  A  U  F  C  P  D  D  V  Z  G  E  M  R  A  W  C  I  F  I  R  R  E  T
S  S  U  P  E  R  I  O  R  D  X  Z  U  E  A  B  Z  W  Z  Z  E  G  R  A  L
```

ACCOMPLISHED	ENJOYABLE	GAINED	KIND	SPACIOUS
ACQUIRED	ENORMOUS	GATHERED	LARGE	SPLENDID
ASTONISHING	ENTERTAINING	GIGANTIC	MAGNIFICENT	SUPERB
ASTOUNDING	EXCELLENT	GLORIOUS	OBTAINED	SUPERIOR
BEHEMOTH	EXCITING	HELPFUL	PLEASANT	TERRIFIC
COLOSSAL	FANTASTIC	HUGE	RECEIVED	WARM
CORDIAL	FESTIVE	INCREDIBLE	RETRIEVED	WONDERFUL
COURTEOUS	FRIENDLY	JOYOUS		

Word Search Time

TOOLS AND EQUIPMENT CONNECTED WITH CAMPING

```
R B O C F B T B L P A V B C F K F S N G W D D W K
F S W R O N O E F C K S F R W T E E T I E I W A J
B Q U A E U N I H B G M R O E I E L L R R D E R O
D I R R L I R A A N T S L E S A L H T T E E O J K
T D R D H E R C I O T L I C K H D O C S T A B E P
S U E S W C K N O T A W J I A C V T S T I E M M G
C R N O O P O T H M A S T F X M A O E S A H K F E
N U O A A S H G H L P F L O C B P R T K A H W Z T
S D L C A P I S K X H E I E O S E F C I N P C S B
U C K E A L R I C A P X T S E T E L I C U A M W T
F G S S H A N H M I F T E R H P H T B R E Q L O E
I G T S M G S M L Q Q G L B I I I B A A E R S B C
R E A Q S E E L N J G L K T L F N N R L T I E O X
T L O T H R O M Y S Q E O U K P I G G U O E F A M
F C I C B W K C W H D V Q B H G W E P B S C G G L
N C T R S K B O Y U G T G Y C N E I D O A H O E E
K A U T Y C O T J Y V S T R T A L E E W L G T H V
M S O V C O M B C U J A P H G D M R D Q O E S X C
H O A C A P E X Z Q W C C N J X R E S H I O T M C
B R S P O O N M V B T J S H Z T A J K L I M D X J
G S M O K E C A M P S L U G F C H N I E G T C K G
S T I C K Z M S E B Z I V F S L P A O S E F I N K
T O W E L K B N F X G S P A I S T N E T S L I A N
P L A T E B A I T F O R K S N D B Z Q V N J T Z I
B O W L M E A T Y X O G I A L U K D B K R E V I R
```

BACKPACK
BAIT
BLANKET
BOARDS
BOOTS
BOULDER
BOWL
BREAD
BRUSH
CAMP
CAMPFIRE
CAPE
CEREAL
CHARCOAL
CHOCOLATE

COMB
COMPASS
CRACKERS
CURRENT
EMBER
FIREWOOD
FISHING POLE
FLASHLIGHT
FORK
FRUIT
GEODE
GRAVY
HAMMER
HATCHET

KETTLE
KNIFE
MARSHMALLOW
MATCHES
MEAT
MILK
MOSQUITO
NAILS
PETRIFIED WOOD
PILLOW
PLATE
RIVER
SEASONING
SLEEPING BAG

SLUG
SMOKE
SOAP
SPOON
STICK
STREAM
SUNSHINE
TENT
TOOTHBRUSH
TOOTHPASTE
TOWEL
VEGETABLE
WALKING STICK
WHISTLE

Word Search Time

Can you find the 55 'cooking' words?

```
B P E S W G U U H O E M I T C S M E M W
A A A K N L R M I X J I S H T E F E E G
N M S R A O I A X U D O I R L G A N R R
Y E T T B B S O T V R L A K R S I I O T
Q L H A E O G A R E L I C O U B L A A P
H T A D K T I R E B N I V R M L S E G M
T Q W D Z J C L E S P A E O W T B J Y S
F P L H Y O J E B A L T C Y R D R H N X
I R C G X H G L R F S E X G T E E A X N
S E M D H Q E B M R U E S A R E C R O A
T W T D N N J E C C O P P P L I E U H C
A O K I D R D G E P S C R A R M N R A S
E L A P E I T B O A S S M E N E A D U S
H R M M U A R A U M W L T A P F A E H P
D C M M E A C T O H N G W E R A R D R I
Q I N H B H E K I U W Z Z Q A I R Y L C
S R E A M X E S B B Y H S A W M N E Q X
I R A W O U K P E E L P R M I Z A A P J
P C H O P J X X D N E C I R E C I D T S
C O O L N Y G P I H W H G I H L I O B E
```

ADD	CHOP	GREASE	MELT	PUREE	SMOKE
BAKE	COMBINE	GRILL	MIX	RICE	SPREAD
BARBECUE	COOL	GRIND	PANFRY	ROAST	STEAM
BASTE	CORRECT	HEAT	PARBOIL	SAUCE	STRAIN
BEAT	CREAM	HIGH	PEEL	SAUTE	THAW
BLEND	DICE	LOW	PICKLE	SEASON	TIME
BOIL	DRAIN	MARINATE	POACH	SHRED	WASH
BROIL	FLAVOR	MEASURE	PREHEAT	SIFT	WHIP
CAN	GRATE	MEDIUM	PREPARE	SIMMER	WHISK
CHILL					

173

Word Search Time

Words that describe tastes, touch, smells, sounds and sights.

```
C J I P N G S E Y S L I P P E R Y F Y B
S R V M R D R E L K Y D A M P X V E L S
T L O V M I P E E A N R V I L E O A H F
G A I O G E C D A I E I R H L O N A R Y
R N N M K N N K E S N U T U G D B O Z E
A O S G Y E I S L T Y G Q S F B S E V B
C O L T Y M D L E Y S Q O S Y T E I U Y
E C A Y T W Z X T R E A U W Y R S R D G
F G S C A J I O D S B U O P B S N E T N
U N H I R T F O S E I K X R A I R J I I
L I I T T Z Z T W B T H K M N E U X D H
T L N N S Z S L U S Z C W G T B Q Y Y C
I G G E Y U V R T S T P E T R Y U E Y U
N R C B Y B N I Z A U H U L Y E G M R O
Y U C P Y T C Y S R E L S R G L T G P T
K G S T H K L T R A C Y T T Y E D T O Y
H I L S Y E I I R I C E R Z A T N D I F
W A E D V N N I O I E L I A W L T V U B
S R B O G G N M P W L U R U O S E U C C
F M L F V G R S S S M E L L I N G T N M
```

BENT	CROOKED	GURGLING	PURRING	SOFT	TART
BITTER	CUDDLY	HEARING	ROASTED	SOUR	TASTING
BLAND	DAMP	ICY	SALTY	SPICY	TIDY
BREEZY	FOGGY	IMMENSE	SEEING	SQUEAL	TINY
BUMPY	FRESH	LOVELY	SHABBY	STALE	TOUCHING
BURNING	FROSTY	MASSIVE	SLASHING	STICKY	VILE
BURNT	FURRY	NEGLECTED	SLIMY	STINKY	WAIL
BUZZ	GOOEY	NUTTY	SLIPPERY	SWEET	WHISTLING
CLUTTERED	GRACEFUL	PRICKLY	SMELLING	TANGY	WISPY
COO	GREASY				

Word Search Time

There are many ways to "fall" down.

```
C E S W S D I S M O U N T D I A Y M M F
P R D W H I N K K M Q M G D N E C S E D
L F A I A I N F O U N D E R T W I E T R
U L R S L M R K C U S Z D E L B M E R T
N U L C H G P L D E L U G E T R V I P V
G C E O U C N E N G U L F D D U E G J S
E T L L C A J W F A X P R E T L A F L F
D U B L C S D P O G L W I J C I J I L C
S A M A H C Q L D D X R Q D P Z P I R E
C T U P P A L U U I K U I C R K P E G T
Z E T S F D V M L W S A C W I L V N S T
R S E E H E T M W N Y I E O T A U A L F
A P T V E O A E M Y D U N R W L O U R W
E I U B G T E T E V Z B R T B C A F A I
P R H R R U R J L F X A D H E S D P P L
P A C T E H U L T I I I P N R G W R H S
A L A G M S L L T N V O W E E C R O O C
S H R M B C I E E E O O M K Z X Y A L P
I G A H U T A P S W R O H N S F G Q T F
D W P D S S F B S D S T O P P L E I D E
```

BREAKDOWN	DISINTEGRATE	FLIP	PLUNGE	SWAMP
CASCADE	DISMOUNT	FLOW	RAIN	SWOOP
COAST	DIVE	FLUCTUATE	SETTLE	TOPPLE
COLLAPSE	DROP	FOUNDER	SINK	TREMBLE
CRASH	DROWN	GLIDE	SLIP	TUMBLE
DELUGE	ENGULF	LUNGE	SOMERSAULT	TWIRL
DESCEND	FAILURE	PARACHUTE	SPIRAL	WAVER
DISAPPEAR	FALTER	PLUMMET	SUBMERGE	WHIRL

Word Search Time

PICK A FLOWER, FRUIT OR VEGETABLE

```
W Q G R R P K W A X D R E O W W U A W S M H N M I
O A B R H E T M F V N A G M R M P Z P K Z P D D R
R P T C E O P W J Y A A M G C A C E F Z W V M O N
C O P E S E D J N P I C I A A O N N W B C C R X A
H T A B R T N O B O I L A N R N V G R K J B A G D
I A N E N M I P D R I N O D E I A C E N Q W X Q M
D T S E C H E U E E U T E C O D G N E S G E E U V
F O Y T Y L P L R P N S A A C C R O A L K A M D C
K P K K B P E V O F P D S N P O U A L B E E P A T
V O M P O T A V Y N E E R E R P R C G D H R N K T
G C J M P B C W Z A K P R O L A L B U T Y T Y O M
H O B O O K H M G E P U A K N S C E N M A H R C M
I O G I K H E M N Q X J U R O K S A P L B R T I U
C O R N P I Y D P S L F Z R G K S P O E A E A H X
U A Y C K Z H I T M P I L U T Y R U R C T E R D I
S P P D E N T A Z P I W I K R E P P A O N U G K J
Y P G T S Y G G E Z S A P H W E O S N I U E N S M
O J G E O X Y M H D C U C O C I P E R L R T P I X
X M B J R A B Q W L P A L H N A C E I A C I S Z A
D N O P T Y V B Q T P F E S R T G D N A N A O M V
A O T I E S S U M R I R E A A N O I B A M U H T G
V G A N L I B U I L R T G R A F U B C A V W U E H
A N M R O A F C U I T U I T F M A H C R P W O J V
U A O U I D O A E I S N P A X G F I N R V U B K F
G M T T V T C S A R E L D W E N J I B U B E I A F
```

APRICOT	CELERY	JICAMA	POINSETTIA
ASPARAGUS	CHERRIES	KIWI	POTATO
AVACADO	CHRYSANTHEMUM	MANGO	RHODODENDRON
BANANA	CORN	MARIGOLD	ROSE
BEET	CUCUMBER	NECTARINE	SPINACH
BROCCOLI	DAFFODIL	ORANGE	TANGERINE
BRUSSELS SPROUTS	DAISY	ORCHID	TOMATO
CABBAGE	GARDENIA	PANSY	TULIP
CANTALOUPE	GERANIUM	PEACH	TURNIP
CARNATION	GRAPEFRUIT	PETUNIA	VIOLET
CARROT	GREEN PEPPER	PINEAPPLE	WATERMELON
CAULIFLOWER	GUAVA		

Word Search Time

Here are almost 50 ways to "GO"!

```
Y R C W M R U O T W O L F T T Y P T L P
T R O D W Q C V E K I H R N R E R E A R
R A C E I S V R B M M A U R L A D R E J
T Z H U P K L A W T M O U B V I A T O S
H R J E C X J Q I P M H M E R D R U C P
I C E N H A R S P E P A L T E E R R R A
D R R A K I I H V E E F S G A N A F I C
S R E A D V F A E G I E W T E M E L D E
L T I D M Y E R A T R T C Y B D R E E R
E B R V N L C Y G I R R P L A Z O E T U
M C E O E A O N T A L R E N J Q A S C N
V E L D L V W E P Q M J E J M Q M T K E
H S A A I L R E A I O M A P W A S E O U
R A A N M S D X H S O A G P N Z A P X R
Y E S U D B A V E R R U S H E K L W Q U
N R C T N E E P P G L T D X D E Q D X Q
A V R E E T R R P L D W N E E R Q K G H
Q M L U D N E F J E A U A U E T M P A S
P U W A C E B R Q R A Z R R A P M X R A
X F C C X S H H D I T R Z T C J S W D D
```

AMBLE	FLEE	MARCH	RETIRE	SCURRY	TREAD
CLAMBER	FLOW	MEANDER	RETREAT	SPEED	TREK
CRAWL	HASTEN	MOUNT	RIDE	STEP	TROD
CREEP	HIKE	PACE	ROAM	STRIDE	TRUDGE
DASH	HURRY	PARADE	RUN	STROLL	VISIT
DEPART	JAUNT	PROMENADE	RUSH	TOUR	VOYAGE
DISAPPEAR	JOURNEY	RACE	SAUNTER	TRAMP	WALK
DRAG	LEAVE	RECEDE	SCRAMBLE	TRAVEL	WANDER
DRIVE					

Word Search Time

MORE THAN 60 WAYS TO SAY "SAID"!

```
A B D D S O B B E D T U O G N A S C X A I S A H P
P G E E E R A G E D D E K R A B O C P L H V X R M
D D O L T T H O W L E D Z G D M A P S U Z Z E D C
R E B N L R T W A I L E D E F X E Y D D D A E R D
E C V L I O U I P Y U B S O B A M D E E C T O E S
P R D E U Z W L M L M S R E L P E L R H R O N M E
L I B E I B E E B E E T S E A R O O E O N A M X E
I E O Q G R B D D F E E D T E S L D T E O D I G T
D S U W D G E O D E T H D N P S E D R P D F J H E
E E K Z U P L H E Z S C I Y L U D R K M M E E D D
D D E I W G E W E D R T J V J A I E E S U D G J
E B D A I D A D O E E E A J V A M V N A F Z G O
R R B T G J N A D D M N S M V J D E E I M U E K
A M G Z S C E E K S K P T P M D D E N R O E B E
O A L Z W C L M S N L N C A R O E E E T T E J D D
R E N E E G A D B P T M I A T E N R R T S E D E B
D E R P G N E D D R O L U V T H A D E E A I D E R
D E T U D R E E E U D P D D E U I T E D D T S W R
D E R E E C K M R E X O L E E L O Z E D P N C N Z
D T D B I E B N R Z Z C Q E L H E D E D G X U I I
S J B O I L E E D E P L E Y A B G D E D X V J H D
L A J R E D D L I L T E D D I D M U Q I N N M F T
J E H D O R A O L C D E L W A B E U A H R A E Y T
R S V G O O T P E W D E I R A E W D M L X C U N N
```

ACCEPTED
ACKNOWLEDGED
AGONIZED
AGREED
ANSWERED
APPEALED TO
BARKED
BAWLED
BEGGED
BELLOWED
BESEECHED
BLUBBERED
BLURTED
BOSSED
COMFORTED
CONSOLED
CRIED

CRIED OUT
CROONED
DEMANDED
DICTATED
EMITTED
EMPATHIZED
ENTREATED
FUMED
GIGGLED
GRIEVED
GROANED
HOWLED
IMPLORED
INSISTED
JABBERED
JOKED
LAMENTED

LAUGHED
LILTED
MIFFED
MOURNED
MUMBLED
ORDERED
PLEADED
PREACHED
PROFESSED
QUAKED
QUIVERED
RAGED
REJOICED
REJOINED
REPLIED
RESPONDED
RETORTED

ROARED
SANG OUT
SCREAMED
SEETHED
SHRIEKED
SHUDDERED
SNIVELED
SOBBED
STAMMERED
STRUGGLED
SYMPATHIZED
THUNDERED
TREMBLED
WAILED
WEARIED
WEPT
YELPED

Word Search Time

More ways to say "pretty", "said", "small" and "really".

```
Y Q R G T W G C S V Q C A I Y G M E T F V H F
Z V N F I U O T W S Z P N L J A X K I A C W A
A L D S L M U S Q Y P C L G R T T Z N I B A N
J X K P P N U D E E R U U V R X I D Y R P N T
D J E A N O E R A E F X E A C T G V Y B C D A
N D C I E W U L D D A L O C R P M F O X D V S
T T N G O T I I A T O R Z C J A G L R T X J T
J G R L A N B E T U D J L K S L C R M V O P I
W O L I G L R R S I H A K G X X Q W B J I E C
G E N E Y D A L N W D O W O J J B T C S O L A
B I A G E C Y A A B H E L F O Z C X M L E A L
M V U Z T X R W N N E I C L U K K D S H T D L
I S D I K I C Y Y N A S L E L I L V Y I E Y
Y P V Y L Q Q E L E G O U P A R L D V S T S X
I E O Y M M R D P L V N U T E R E Y E E E S M
B E F J Y Y J F V T U I I N I R E D W B P I V
H A Q X S L Z K C X I F T T C F E D J K B H W
B U S X N W E X T J M O R U N E U D G M H A K
V N H J M S T L I J G T N E N A D L O A G H G
E E C D J V J U O J M X Y A D I H M C H A S X
R T R O F C O L K P Y N U P L N M C X A Y J Z
T R I T E O P W M A B Y N J D L O I N H H Y R
M T G J Z A V M X S Y L E V O L Y W D E W A S
```

ANNOUNCED	DIMINUTIVE	GORGEOUS	PETITE
APPEALING	DREADFULLY	GULPED	PUNY
ATTRACTIVE	ENCHANTING	HISSED	STUNNING
AWFULLY	EXCEPTIONALLY	HOLLERED	TINY
BEAUTIFUL	EXTRAORDINARILY	INCREDIBLY	TRITE
BELLOWED	FAIR	LOVELY	WHISPERED
COMPACT	FANTASTICALLY	MARVELOUSLY	WONDERFULLY
DECLARED	GABBED	MINIATURE	

Word Search Time

PICK A SPORT, JUST ANY SPORT!

```
P T G I Z B B D C X B Y I U S N P P S X Y Y E O J
U E O Z P Y O F O W N E Z A T O N C G K W X R G O R
R N L O U N E X H Y A H J S L M F G G N A H Z Y R W
O N F B H R P K I H Q T D E O K H T N N I T T R W
U I P L D P I T C N O P E U N D L U B I I T I G W Z
V S R G M K G D F O G T N R G O G L R A L T N N Z
T J G U S H V R Z K H T A S S Y T N A D L B A U G
L B Z A Q I Z D W B A G H I P K M N I B L L M O H
S T O F N R S M K I N A K S R E I N I L T I Z U B
P P E U Y X T R N I N Z P W B B E I A M T O N P T
O M F I R A U C L G L E A A H L A D N S D S O G R
R K T W G E L I G L L T S A A S Y L S G T A E F T
E X F F L I B L L U E E N C W A B A L K R I B R I
C T U Y M O I A N R B D R I C E Z G N O A C C C W
C J G B M D B K P A B O M H B W E E I G O T Z S V
O N I W I T I O L A S M T Z C N O C D G N N I L J
S N O N E N L L L S I I T V E N M H Q E N I I N P
G N G K G O S L E N N Q I G F D D O T P L I V N G
S N S L J U G G G G F K I B G Y Z Z M J L M W I G
J A Y E R N N H D G L X S G U X G N Y N M L Y O D
B F B F I I I I N V Y L Q P P H Z G U Y B G U R R
B E I G L K S I O Y P E L T L U U M G G N I I K S
Z N G C I C C S K A T E B O A R D I N G T C M D K
G O Y N U A J A V E L I N T H R O W I N G S U J P
J C G S R H O R S E B A C K R I D I N G A O H N N
```

BADMINTON
BASEBALL
BASKETBALL
BOATING
BOXING
CYCLING
DISCUS
DIVING
FOOTBALL
GOLF
GYMNASTICS
HANDBALL
HANG GLIDING
HIKING

HOCKEY
HORSEBACK RIDING
HOT AIR BALLOONING
HUNTING
HURDLING
JAVELIN THROWING
JOGGING
LACROSSE
MOUNTAIN CLIMBING
RACING
ROWING
RUGBY
SKATEBOARDING
SKATING

SKIING
SNOWMOBILING
SOCCER
SOFTBALL
SPEED SKATING
SPELUNKING
SURFING
SWIMMING
TENNIS
TUMBLING
WATER POLO
WATER SKIING
WRESTLING
YACHTING

180

Word Search Time

Can you find the 49 words about spring in this puzzle?

```
Q O E O J T B L W A C X Y F E B F Y J N G I Q
B Y G K E I I A D E S E S E I M R L E M A P Y
F R O M C D T N L P B S W P N M E E U S H Y C
A V L Y O E A E R R E D I K L I O R E F R O C
I E C F R L S I I N T S A P N A H S A Z F E P
H L F F S T N L T L J E A C F T N S S L Y Y J
E A A S I G L H I D L S T F G L H T N O D J J
D L A A T I G Y C B T A W H G N L G I U L S K
L R L I A I R E L U J M B D E N I A I N S B Q
G D M N R E L O R P R S E T R R I L B L G B J
L E C B H C W E G A P W Q A E A B L H E Y Q T
N E G T I I F L B I B Y K G D K O A G C S A Z
I X A S N L K B K L N P G X F O S B L D T A D
N E P G O N I E W Q R H N H F L W A E L E A B
F O U W E T S O J U B I K J W X X S B T E L H
P J E T P E G I J L K F V S K C U M O E A P F
C R T T U L I P T W U L U J K L L N X C T K V
J I O O Z E O V K I J Y E P V E C N E F C P S
K L A W N Q W B A N I N M A O P M O O L B E U
G R E E N E A A B F R D R I T Z N Y M L A B R
S P R I N G L E A F Y E O U X I I P G K S W J
S T A R R Y R O B I N E W L M E N T V H K T B
H Y X V K E D F T F T S H S U L S W O L L E Y
```

BALMY	CELESTIAL	GREEN	PASTURE	SPRING
BASEBALL	DAFFODIL	HATCHLING	PLANTING	SPRINGTIME
BASKETBALL	DAYLIGHT	HELMET	POPSICLE	STARRY
BICYCLE	EMERALD	JERSEY	RABBIT	SUNSHINE
BLOOM	FEATHERY	KITTEN	ROBIN	TETHERBALL
BLOSSOM	FENCE	LAWN	SEED	TULIP
BLOWING	FLEDGLING	LEAFY	SKATEBOARD	WATERFALL
BREEZY	FLOWER	MEADOW	SLUSH	WORM
BRIGHTNESS	FLUFFY	MUCK	SOCCER	YELLOW
BRILLIANCE	GRASSLAND	OOZE	SPIKES	

181

Word Search Time

THERE ARE 62 WORDS ABOUT SUMMER IN THIS PUZZLE.

```
P P S S S B B O E P D X T R U G H F T E N T N T X
A I C P Y E A R I K S W F H A S A E E I W P S N A
R C O L N E L L E N F E R J U S T G K S X S N M B
A N R A P O N B L E T I X B Y S P R O A T D C O W
D I C S A E I R B O Z M V P H R K B E R B I D B T
E C H H T I E T U U O Y E N E D R R E A F M V D S
Z B S H I H L J O O B N O N F D N E O R M L A A R
F L A Q O M V J H L J I C G T S I U B W R E L L L
V I L L W Y R R O N T E S M I P C T O W E Y R U C
X M T I O D J V L A L K J M Z A F G I R A R L S B
D P Y H K N X X E E J X M Y R L S S N O G R I X H
N H C D P I I R B R K E G N O K T P E I N P T F E
O X U L O W C R N H R F I A E A S N L A H L M S G
P Z U A S E A O R I U V T S N W N C O A S C N A R
R T I C R T I E N O A I X D I H R C O I T H R C C
E L I S I S G G L L N A A M Q R O S F N T T E A T
M O B O R R R E C G S U M J M O U O L G C A E L M
M O N U U E U O M S G I D U K N R A W O N E C R L
U P C B T C N O R N N N G O B E G Y F X X I R A J
S X M S E F U O I G A N U U S O G G C E D G K T V
E A I B E N O L C L I T R T O N V L N E D I T I P
H L R T T D Z Q D N Q N G N I X J G O Y A R P S H
B A T A T Z N O R P F X M T J A U N T X T Y S H Q
B I I U I Q O U O F C W U T R E K W Q H E S U O D
Y N O S Z W B O G I Y O B E A C H B A L M I H S X
```

BALLOON	CLAMBAKE	JAUNT	POND	SPRAY
BALM	CONCERT	JOURNEY	POOL	STRAWBERRY
BARBECUE	CONFETTI	LAGOON	RASPBERRY	STREAMERS
BEACH	COOKOUT	LOTION	RECREATION	SUMMER
BLIMP	DOUSE	MARCHING	SALTY	SUNBURN
BLISTER	EXCURSION	MOUNTAIN	SCALD	SWIMMING
BREEZY	EXPEDITION	OINTMENT	SCORCH	TENT
BUBBLES	FESTIVAL	OUTDOORS	SEASHELL	TIDE
BULLFROG	FIREWORKS	OUTING	SIMMERING	TREK
BURNING	FLOATING	PARADE	SIZZLING	VACATION
CAMPGROUND	FOREST	PATIO	SPLASH	WINDY
CARNIVAL	HAMBURGER	PICNIC	SPLATTER	WOODLAND
CELEBRATION	HIKING			

182

Word Search Time

60 WINTER WORDS!

```
J C C W M D S R F R O S T Q E T F D Y W O N S C C
O T O H M A R T E U E J S T O Y S U E W M G A A F
L U N O I C R E O L S Z H E Y E U Y W L U R R A H
L R O B K M D Z S C A G F R I F G F B V O O M U M
Y K E E A I N R I S K T N D N T T Y U L L I M T E
W E L L N H E E E P I I I I E O I U S E L B R R R
L Y D L N A A S Y E A N N V T V I V R Y U Q R E R
C C A S T T M R N N D N G G E E E T I G Y B I E Y
C A C R E X C W O W H N J X S S E R A T L X Y H Y
C R K E W F I V O N X K I V A D Z R G R S N L M X
S D B Y V H I Z O N E S P E Q H P M G R O E W E A
R S N C G P Z K N K S M P G R G I S C C E C F H G
S S S X C F V R S L A R I F H S N H C G H E E E Q
H A T E K M B X Q S O N L Q T O E T I A V U N D L
T L F X J E Y M M G G M W L W E Q L N A N I R N T
A A I K Y C B N R E T M E F R A E G C E E D R C L
E D G C L A Z A R Y E T L F H W Z A C F M K L S H
R H R I L E M B R C O A U R Y S T O G E R A U E G
W K E S O P R R A E K L E T T I N S Y A L O N M S
L B T U H E E L H E M T I N O C D A E R R G S R U
E O N M A B P G I E H V E N E N D N H L I L N T O
S B I D N E I K M G I S O R E I T B B L P B A I Y
N V W A R E E O U T E N T I L T C A L K M M B N J
I B R I L G R A A R E O R O U G S N J I N Z E O D
T C F S E Y L N P O H F H H Y M N P A V P O W T N
```

BELLS	DRESSING	HOLIDAY	MUSIC	SNOWFLAKE
CANDLES	EVERGREEN	HOLLY	NATIVITY	SNOWMAN
CARDS	FAMILY	HUMBUG	NOEL	SNOWY
CAROLER	FESTIVITIES	HYMN	ORNAMENT	STOCKINGS
CAROLS	FIREPLACE	JINGLE	PEACE	TEMPLE
CHEERFUL	FRIENDS	JOLLY	PRESENTS	TINSEL
CHIMNEY	FROST	LAUGHTER	PROGRAM	TOYS
CHURCH	FROSTY	MARZIPAN	REINDEER	TREE
CONCERT	GARLAND	MEMORY	RELATIVES	TURKEY
COOKIES	GIFTS	MENORAH	RIBBON	VACATION
CRANBERRY	GINGERBREAD	MERRY	SALAD	WINTER
DECORATION	GREETINGS	MISTLETOE	SLEIGH	WREATH

183

Key
Wordsearch
Go, Fall, Cooking, Autumn

Here are almost 50 ways to "GO"!

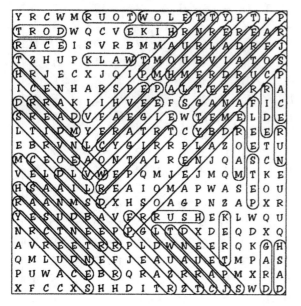

There are many ways to "fall" down.

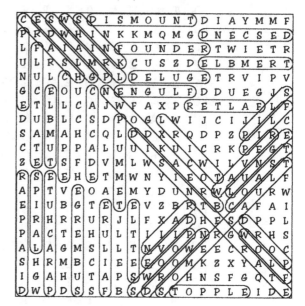

Can you find the 55 'cooking' words?

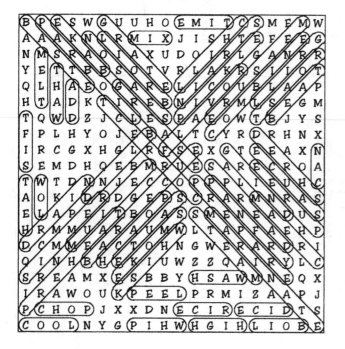

Find 50 words about autumn.

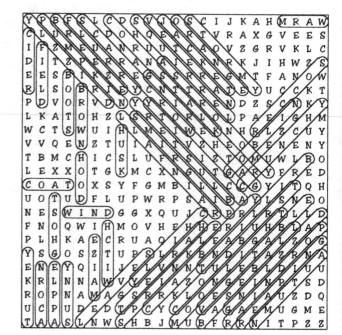

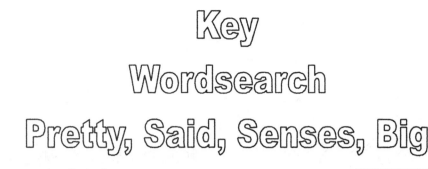

Key
Wordsearch
Pretty, Said, Senses, Big

More ways to say "pretty", "said", "small" and "really".

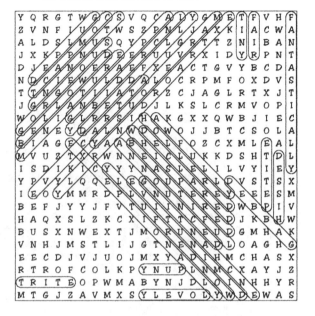

MORE THAN 60 WAYS TO SAY "SAID"!

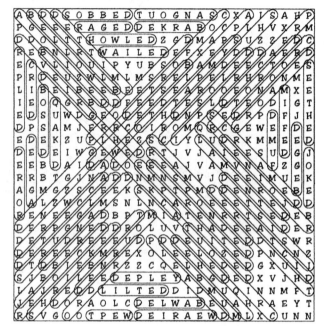

Words that describe tastes, touch, smells, sounds and sights.

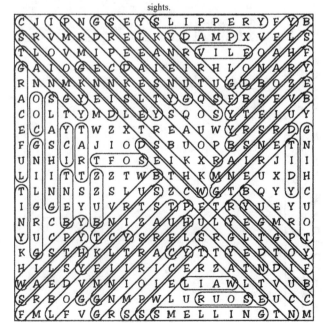

OTHER WAYS TO SAY "BIG", "NICE", "GOOD" and "GOT"

Key
Wordsearch
Flowers, Sports, Camping

PICK A FLOWER, FRUIT OR VEGETABLE

PICK A SPORT, JUST ANY SPORT!

TOOLS AND EQUIPMENT CONNECTED WITH CAMPING

60 WINTER WORDS!

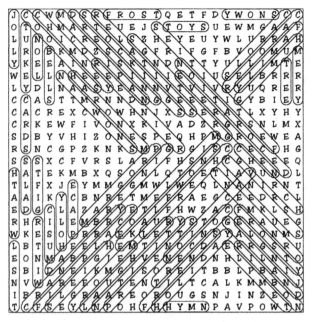

Can you find the 49 words about spring in this puzzle?

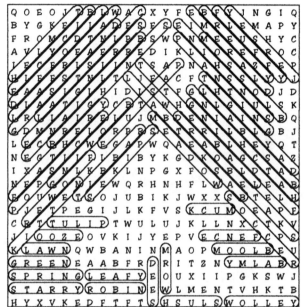

THERE ARE 62 WORDS ABOUT SUMMER IN THIS PUZZLE.

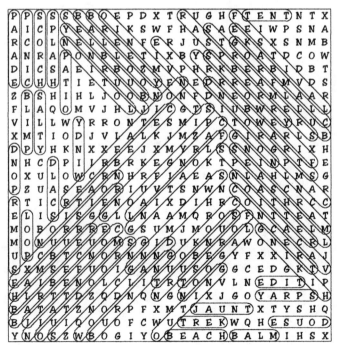

Word Sorts

Vocabulary, Finding Alternatives For "Tired Words"

These puzzles are most appropriate for:

✳
✳✳
✳✳✳

Word Sort #1

Figure out which words belong in each category and write them on the lines.

colossal	enormous	gigantic	huge	behemoth
large	spacious	huge	enjoyable	entertaining
exciting	fantastic	festive	incredible	joyous
splendid	accomplished	gathered	gained	acquired
gained	obtained	received	retrieved	astonishing
excellent	astounding	magnificent	glorious	superb
superior	terrific	wonderful	courteous	cordial
friendly	helpful	kind	pleasant	warm

Big   Nice   Good   Got

_____ _____ _____ _____

_____ _____ _____ _____

_____ _____ _____ _____

_____ _____ _____ _____

_____ _____ _____ _____

_____ _____ _____ _____

_____ _____ _____ _____

_____ _____ _____ _____

_____ _____ _____ _____

Word Sort #2

Figure out which words belong in each category and write them on the lines.

carrot	daffodil	cantaloupe	marigold	corn
violet	pineapple	gardenia	carnation	turnip
tangerine	asparagus	guava	celery	nectarine
cucumber	orange	poinsettia	apricot	chrysanthemum
banana	cabbage	spinach	tulip	petunia
mango	orchid	daisy	peach	broccoli
watermelon	geranium	cauliflower	kiwi	rose
jicama	potato	tomato	beet	avacado

Fruits   Vegetables   Flowers

_____ _____ _____

_____ _____ _____

_____ _____ _____

_____ _____ _____

_____ _____ _____

_____ _____ _____

_____ _____ _____

_____ _____ _____

_____ _____ _____

_____ _____ _____

Word Sort #3

Figure out which words belong in each category and write them on the lines.

appealing	attractive	beautiful	enchanting
fair	gorgeous	lovely	stunning
announced	declared	gabbed	hissed
bellowed	hollered	whispered	gulped
compact	diminutive	trite	miniature
petite	puny	tiny	awfully
dreadfully	exceptionally	extraordinarily	fantastically
incredibly	marvelously	wonderfully	

Pretty   Said   Small   Really

_____   _____   _____   _____

_____   _____   _____   _____

_____   _____   _____   _____

_____   _____   _____   _____

_____   _____   _____   _____

_____   _____   _____   _____

_____   _____   _____   _____

Word Sort #4

Figure out which words belong in each category and write them on the lines.

touching	breezy	bumpy	cuddly	damp
frosty	furry	gooey	greasy	icy
prickly	slimy	slippery	soft	sticky
seeing	bent	burnt	cluttered	crooked
foggy	graceful	immense	lovely	massive
neglected	shabby	tidy	tiny	wispy
hearing	buzz	coo	gurgling	purring
slashing	squeal	wail	whistling	smelling
burning	fresh	salty	roasted	stale
stinky	sweet	vile	tasting	bitter
bland	nutty	salty	sour	spicy
tangy	tart			

See

_____

_____

_____

_____

_____

_____

_____

_____

_____

_____

_____

Taste

_____

_____

_____

_____

_____

_____

_____

_____

_____

_____

_____

Hear

_____

_____

_____

_____

_____

_____

_____

_____

_____

_____

_____

Smell

_____

_____

_____

_____

_____

_____

_____

_____

_____

_____

_____

Feel

_____

_____

_____

_____

_____

_____

_____

_____

_____

_____

_____

Word Quakes

**Making words from a given set of letters.
Word Chunking, Vocabulary Expansion**

These puzzles are most appropriate for:

$$*$$
$$**$$
$$***$$

Word Quake

This is an easy game. See how many words you can build using only the letters from the given word. The letters can be in any order, but a letter may not be used more times than it is used in the original word.
No foreign words, no abbreviations and no proper nouns!
If you need more space, use the back of the paper.

accidental

Word Quake

This is an easy game. See how many words you can build using only the letters from the given word. The letters can be in any order, but a letter may not be used more times than it is used in the original word.
No foreign words, no abbreviations and no proper nouns!
If you need more space, use the back of the paper.

anticipation

Word Quake

This is an easy game. See how many words you can build using only the letters from the given word. The letters can be in any order, but a letter may not be used more times than it is used in the original word.
No foreign words, no abbreviations and no proper nouns!
If you need more space, use the back of the paper.

atmosphere

Word Quake

This is an easy game. See how many words you can build using only the letters from the given word. The letters can be in any order, but a letter may not be used more times than it is used in the original word.
No foreign words, no abbreviations and no proper nouns!
If you need more space, use the back of the paper.

consternation

Word Quake

This is an easy game. See how many words you can build using only the letters from the given word. The letters can be in any order, but a letter may not be used more times than it is used in the original word.
No foreign words, no abbreviations and no proper nouns!
If you need more space, use the back of the paper.

destination

Word Quake

This is an easy game. See how many words you can build using only the letters from the given word. The letters can be in any order, but a letter may not be used more times than it is used in the original word.
No foreign words, no abbreviations and no proper nouns!
If you need more space, use the back of the paper.

incidentally

Word Quake

This is an easy game. See how many words you can build using only the letters from the given word. The letters can be in any order, but a letter may not be used more times than it is used in the original word.
No foreign words, no abbreviations and no proper nouns!
If you need more space, use the back of the paper.

intelligent

Word Quake

This is an easy game. See how many words you can build using only the letters from the given word. The letters can be in any order, but a letter may not be used more times than it is used in the original word.
No foreign words, no abbreviations and no proper nouns!
If you need more space, use the back of the paper.

intentional

Word Quake

This is an easy game. See how many words you can build using only the letters from the given word. The letters can be in any order, but a letter may not be used more times than it is used in the original word.
No foreign words, no abbreviations and no proper nouns!
If you need more space, use the back of the paper.

international

Word Quake

This is an easy game. See how many words you can build using only the letters from the given word. The letters can be in any order, but a letter may not be used more times than it is used in the original word.
No foreign words, no abbreviations and no proper nouns!
If you need more space, use the back of the paper.

measurable

Word Quake

This is an easy game. See how many words you can build using only the letters from the given word. The letters can be in any order, but a letter may not be used more times than it is used in the original word.
No foreign words, no abbreviations and no proper nouns!
If you need more space, use the back of the paper.

metropolis

Word Quake

This is an easy game. See how many words you can build using only the letters
from the given word. The letters can be in any order, but a letter may not be used
more times than it is used in the original word.
No foreign words, no abbreviations and no proper nouns!
If you need more space, use the back of the paper.

multiplication

Word Quake

This is an easy game. See how many words you can build using only the letters from the given word. The letters can be in any order, but a letter may not be used more times than it is used in the original word.
No foreign words, no abbreviations and no proper nouns!
If you need more space, use the back of the paper.

p e r f o r m a n c e

Word Quake

This is an easy game. See how many words you can build using only the letters from the given word. The letters can be in any order, but a letter may not be used more times than it is used in the original word.
No foreign words, no abbreviations and no proper nouns!
If you need more space, use the back of the paper.

photography

Word Quake

This is an easy game. See how many words you can build using only the letters from the given word. The letters can be in any order, but a letter may not be used more times than it is used in the original word.
No foreign words, no abbreviations and no proper nouns!
If you need more space, use the back of the paper.

transportation

Word Quake

This is an easy game. See how many words you can build using only the letters from the given word. The letters can be in any order, but a letter may not be used more times than it is used in the original word.
No foreign words, no abbreviations and no proper nouns!
If you need more space, use the back of the paper.

undecided

Word Hunt

**Finding words hidden within a sentence.
Word Chunking, Vocabulary Expansion**

These puzzles are most appropriate for:

**
***

Mystery Animals

The name of an animal is hidden in each sentence. They may be hidden in two or more words. Can you find each one?

1) Please allow enough time to see all the circus acts tonight.

2) You might see a dog named Bob catch a ball on his nose.

3) Bob will throw the ball to a seal named Adolph in the center ring.

4) The penguin act came later in the show.

5) Water animals move with awkwardness on land.

6) The fuzzy monkey wore a cap each time he swung across the ring.

7) I am still amazed at the tricks the animals learned!

8) As the running lion began to pant, her pace slowed.

There are TWO animals hidden in each of these sentences. They may be hidden in one or several words. Look carefully!

1) The new balloon I bought stands out in a crowd.

2) An artist was painting a portrait on a large yellow easel.

3) Leo, pardon me, please, so I can see the elephant better.

4) The new dog needs a set of bowls for his food.

5) There are a million things to do rather than clean the bathtub.

6) We'll hear the fireworks go "bang" or I'll arrange another trip to the fair.

7) Bob is on time, and he promises to be a really good audience.

8) Put your coin in the slot here and there will be a very short game to play.

Hidden Bugs

The names of various bugs or other small, crawly creatures are hidden in each sentence. They may be hidden in two or more words. Can you find each one?

1) I found a marvelous costume with the Mardi Gras shop person's help.

2) The student relaxed when he saw the midterm items listed were very familiar.

3) The Black Knight knocked him down in the joust and our hero ached all over.

4) Why would we be excited about another two hours worth of homework?

5) The forward ran, determined to kick the rolling rubber ball into the goal.

6) The chef mixed the waffle and pancake batter in two separate bowls.

7) Another graph idea is to survey the class about their preferences for pizza.

8) Pioneers would make soap using a liquid form of lye from wood ashes and other fatty acids.

There are TWO bugs hidden in each of these sentences. They may be hidden in one or several words. Look carefully!

9) Many people enjoy experiencing nature and have been on many camping trips.

10) Mary pulled hard on the beet, let go unexpectedly, and nearly lost her cap hiding in the weeds.

11) I saw the butter fly across the table when the syrup container was partially tipped over.

Write your own sentence hiding a "buggy" word. You can use one of the words from these puzzles, or come up with your own.

Sentence:

_____

Hidden word: _____

Secret Games

The name of a game or piece of game equipment is hidden in each sentence. They may be hidden in two or more words. Can you find each one?

1) Get the sword, search for any more weapons and seize the horse.

2) Far, far away there was a magical kingdom in Oregon where trolls ruled the highways and bridges.

3) When you are in Scotland, don't forget to go to the shop "Scotch Bagpipes Are Us".

4) The tiny baby cub attacked the butterfly with vigorous energy.

5) As they went across, word came that the carnival was just beyond the river.

6) The hiker was grateful the matches stayed dry after the backpack tumbled into the creek.

There are TWO games, or game pieces, hidden in each of these sentences. They may be hidden in one or several words. Look carefully!

7) Omar blessed the prince with a silver comb attached to a golden chain.

8) The shop awning was striped black in gray background.

Write your own sentence hiding a "gamey" word. You can use one of the words from these puzzles, or come up with your own.

Sentence:

_____

Hidden word: _____

Space Treasure

The names of planets or other astronomical words are hidden, one in each sentence. They may be hidden in two or more words. Can you find each one?

1) There are seven uses for rattlesnake oil.

2) I felt very heart-heavy when my best friend moved away.

3) I would like you to come to the fair with me.

4) Many people don't understand the harm arson can do.

5) The gnu ran using all of its speed to avoid the cheetah.

6) The best area to see the finest view is at the edge of the Grand Canyon.

7) When the winter rain stops, the air is very clean.

8) There are no vacations with pay for people without jobs.

There are TWO astronomy words hidden in each of these sentences. They may be hidden in one or several words. Look carefully!

9) The king had to mete oranges or bits of them to make sure everyone got some.

10) If you go to the Leaning Tower of Pisa, turn left and moo nine times, your wish will come true.

Write your own sentence hiding a "spacey" word. You can use one of the words from these puzzles, or come up with your own.

Sentence:

_____

Hidden word: _____

Fruit Puzzles

The name of a fruit is hidden in each sentence. They may be hidden in two or more words. Can you find each one?

1)   I want you to help each other with this project.

2)   Make sure you have ample money when you go to the fair.

3)   In the Bahamas we stayed at a cabana named "Heaven."

4)   To live here is great!

5)   My aunt is a landscape artist who enjoys using watercolors.

6)   We watched the really tall man go down the street.

7)   I last talked to my cousin Tom at Ohio State.

8)   Sam had to grapple with his dog to get her to come home again.

There are TWO fruits hidden in each of these sentences. They may be hidden in one or several words. Look carefully!

9)   The plumber came to my house to remove the slime.

10) In my personal management class, I learned to target anger, ineptitude, and panic, and to control my own fears or anger.

Write your own sentence hiding a "fruity" word. You can use one of the words from these puzzles, or come up with your own.

Sentence:

_____

Hidden word: _____

Key to Hidden Words Puzzles

Mystery Animals

1) Plea<u>se all</u>ow enough time to see all the circus acts tonight.

2) You might see a dog named <u>Bob cat</u>ch a ball on his nose.

3) Bob will throw the ball to a seal named A<u>dolph in</u> the center ring.

4) The penguin act <u>came l</u>ater in the show.

5) Water animals move wit<u>h awk</u>wardness on land.

6) The woolly monkey wore a c<u>ap e</u>ach time he swung across the ring.

7) I am stil<u>l amaz</u>ed at the tricks the animals learned!

8) As the running lion began to <u>pant, her</u> pace slowed.

1) The new bal<u>loon</u> I bought stands out in a <u>crow</u>d.

2) An artist <u>was p</u>ainting a portrait on a large yello<u>w easel</u>.

3) <u>Leo, pard</u>on me, please, so I can see th<u>e el</u>ephant better.

4) <u>The new</u> dog needs a set of b<u>owl</u>s for his food.

5) There are a mil<u>lion</u> things to do rather than clean the <u>bat</u>htub.

6) We'll hear the <u>clam</u>orous fireworks go "ban<u>g" or I'll</u> arrange another trip to the fair.

7) <u>Bob is on</u> time, and he promises to <u>be a r</u>eally good audience.

8) Put your coin in the <u>slot here</u> and there will <u>be a ver</u>y short game to play.

Hidden Bugs

9) I found a marvelous costume with the Mardi <u>Gras shop per</u>son's help.

10) The student relaxed when he saw the mid<u>term item</u>s listed were very familiar.

11) The Black Knight knocked him down in the joust and our h<u>ero ached</u> all over.

12) Why would we <u>be e</u>xcited about another two hours worth of homework?

13) The forward ran, determined to kick the rolling <u>rub</u>ber ball into the goal.

14) The chef mixed the wa<u>ffle a</u>nd pancake batter in two separate bowls.

15) Another g<u>raph idea</u> is to survey the class about their preferences for pizza.

16) Pioneers would make soap using a liquid form of <u>lye</u> from wood ashes and other fatty acids.

12) Many people enjoy experiencin<u>g nature</u> and have <u>been</u> on many camping trips.

13) Mary pulled hard on the <u>beet, let</u> go unexpectedly and nearly lost her <u>cap hiding</u> in the weeds.

14) I saw the <u>butter fly</u> across the table when the syrup container <u>was p</u>artially tipped over.

Secret Games

7) Get the s<u>word, search</u> for any more weapons and seize the horse.

8) Far, far away there was a magical king<u>dom in Orego</u>n where trolls ruled the highways and bridges.

9) When you are in Scotland, don't forget to go to the <u>shop "Scotch</u> Bagpipes Are Us".

10) The tiny baby cu<u>b at</u>tacked the butterfly with vigorous energy.

11) As they went a<u>cross, word</u> came that the carnival was just beyond the river.

12) The hiker was grateful the ma<u>tches s</u>tayed dry after the backpack tumbled into the creek.

11) O<u>mar bles</u>sed the prince with a silver com<u>b at</u>tached to a golden chain.

12) The sho<u>p awn</u>ing was striped blac<u>k in g</u>ray background.

Space Treasure

9) There are se<u>ven us</u>es for rattlesnake oil.

10) I felt very h<u>eart h</u>eavy when my best friend moved away.

11) I would like you to <u>come t</u>o the fair with me.

12) Many people don't understand the ha<u>rm ars</u>on can do.

13) The gn<u>u ran us</u>ing all of its speed to avoid the cheetah.

14) The be<u>st area</u> to see the finest view is at the edge of the Grand Canyon.

15) When the win<u>ter ra</u>in stops, the air is very clean.

16) There are <u>no vac</u>ations with pay for people without jobs.

13) The king had to <u>mete or</u>anges <u>or bit</u>s of them to make sure everyone got some.

14) If you go to the Leaning Tower of P<u>isa, turn</u> left and <u>moo n</u>ine times, your wish will come true.

Fruit Puzzles

9) I want you to hel<u>p each</u> other with this project.

10) Make sure you have amp<u>le mone</u>y when you go to the fair.

11) In the Bahamas we stayed at a ca<u>bana nam</u>ed "Heaven."

12) T<u>o live</u> here is great!

13) My aunt is a landsca<u>pe art</u>ist who enjoys using water colors.

14) We watched the really tall <u>man go</u> down the street.

15) I last talked to my cousin <u>Tom at O</u>hio State.

16) Sam had to gr<u>apple</u> with his dog to get her to come home again.

11) The <u>plumber</u> came to my house to remove the s<u>lime</u>.

12) In my personal management class, I learned to targe<u>t anger, i</u>neptitude and panic, and to control my own fears <u>or anger</u>.

Classroom Helps

✳
✳✳
✳✳✳

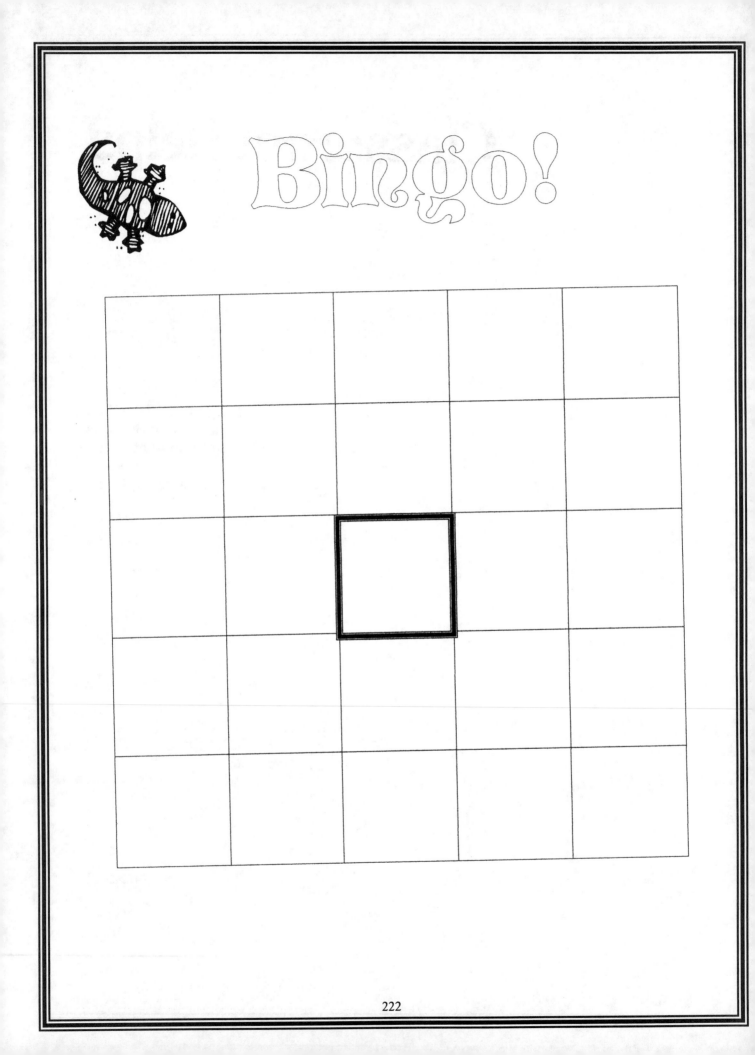

Bingo!

Possible Reading Slogans:

Reading Is Cool!

You're The Reading
Generation!

Reading Is Fun!

Dare To Dream The Future:
Read

Read With A Friend!

Off To See The World:
Read!

Reading:
It's The Real Thing!

Reading:
Everything To Gain.

Born To Read!

Reading:
Just For The Fun Of It!

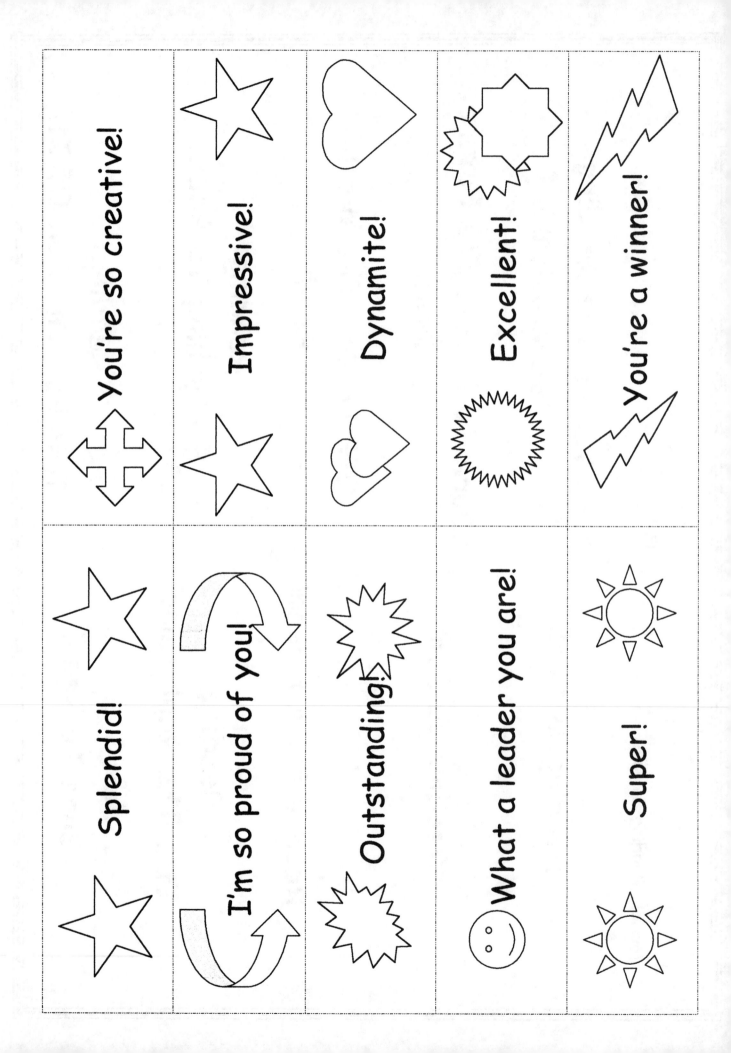

You're so creative!

Impressive!

Dynamite!

Excellent!

You're a winner!

Splendid!

I'm so proud of you!

Outstanding!

What a leader you are!

Super!

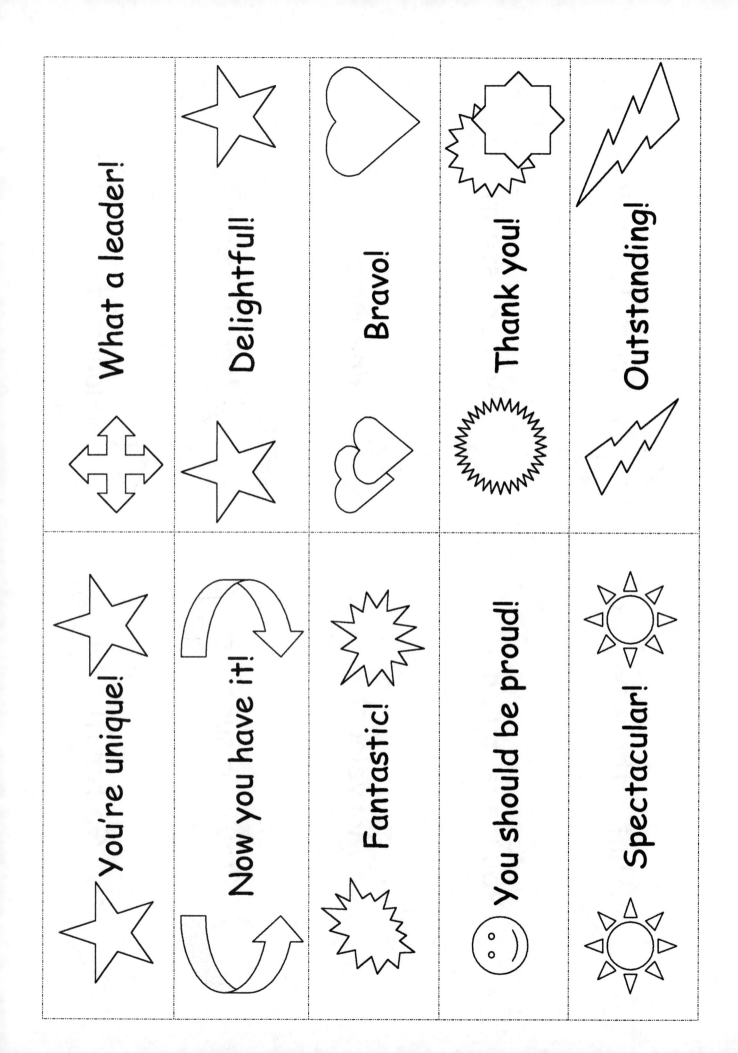

What a leader!

Delightful!

Bravo!

Thank you!

Outstanding!

You're unique!

Now you have it!

Fantastic!

You should be proud!

Spectacular!

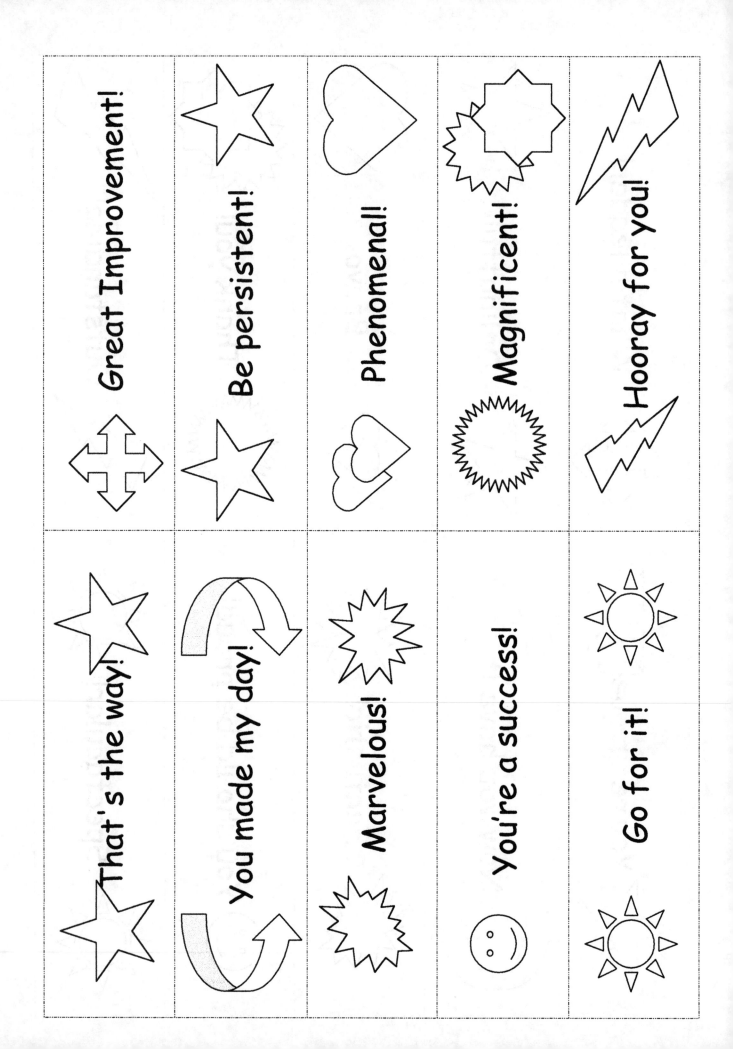

Great Improvement!

Be persistent!

Phenomenal!

Magnificent!

Hooray for you!

That's the way!

You made my day!

Marvelous!

You're a success!

Go for it!

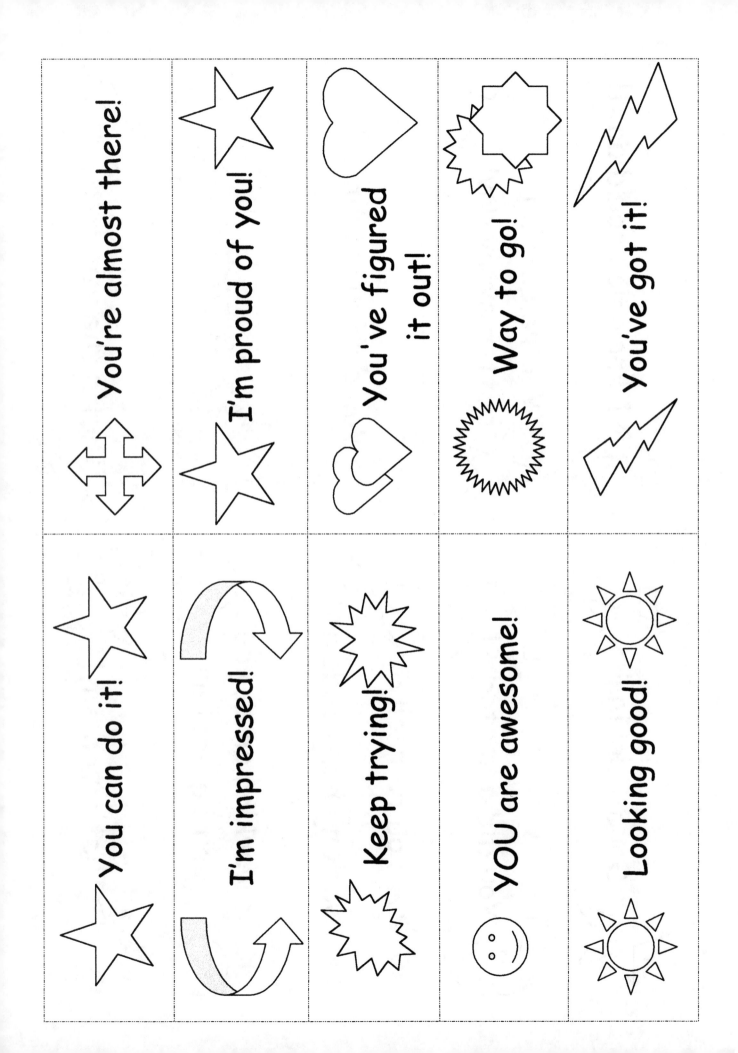

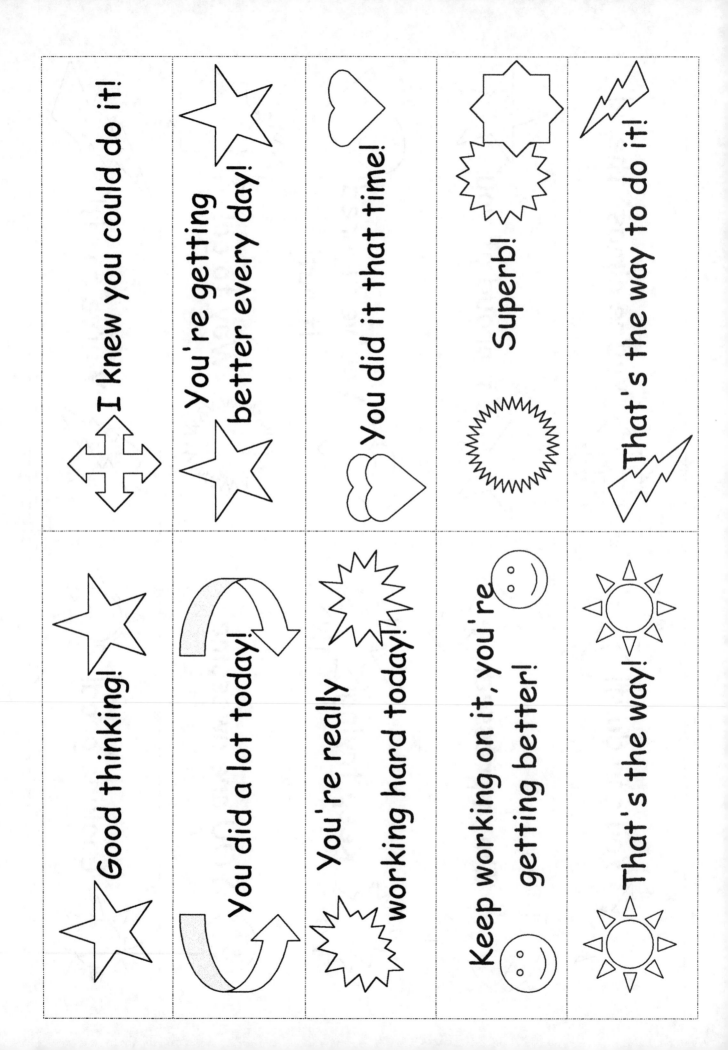

I knew you could do it!

You're getting better every day!

You did it that time!

Superb!

That's the way to do it!

Good thinking!

You did a lot today!

You're really working hard today!

Keep working on it, you're getting better!

That's the way!

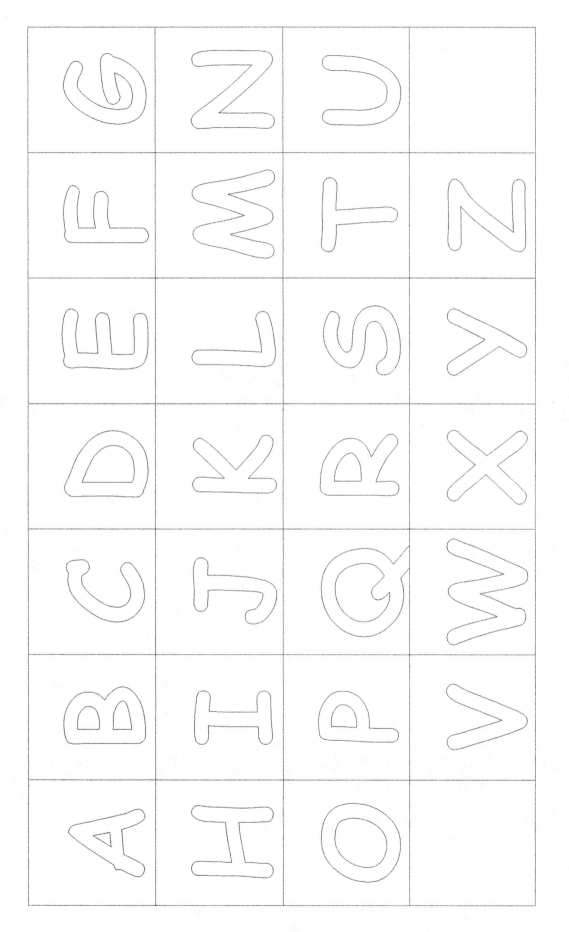

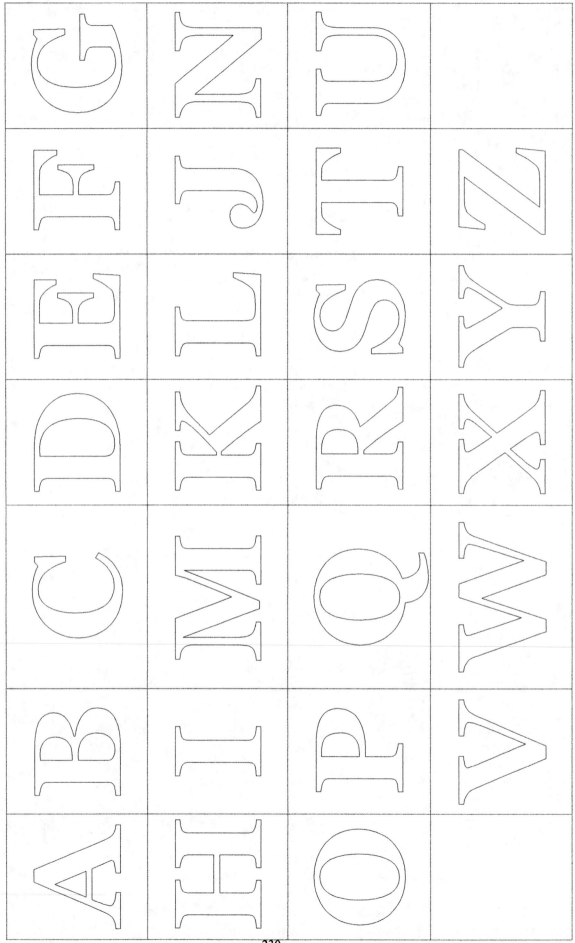

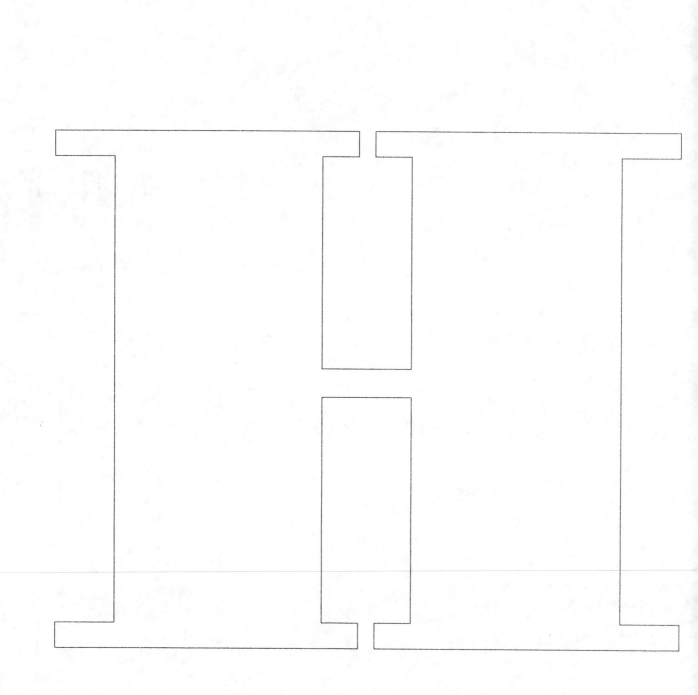

238

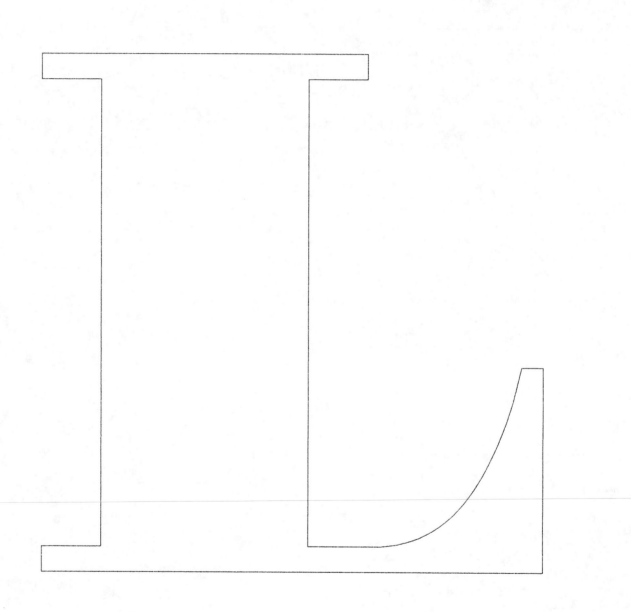

246

247

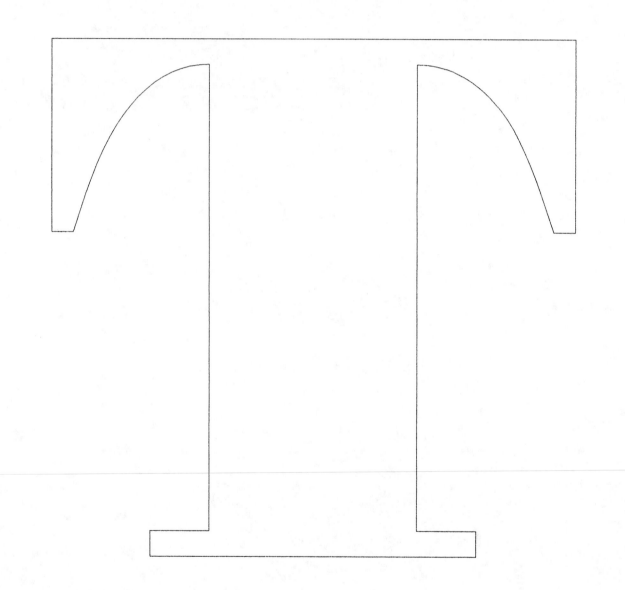

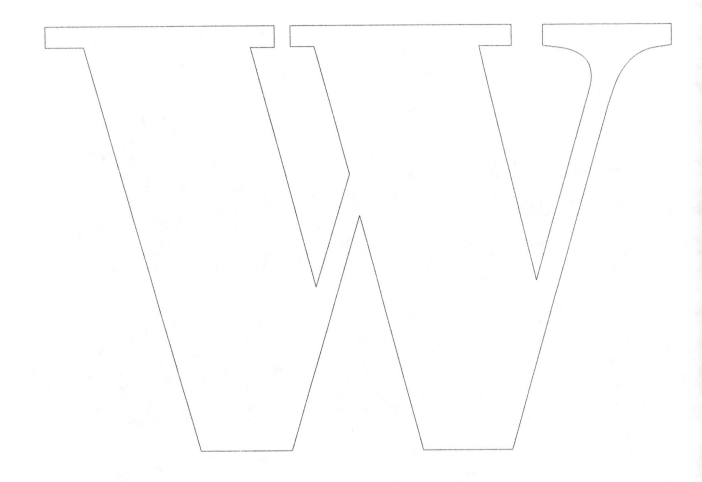